FOUNDATION ENGINEERING

BY

WEST'S PILING

NOTES ON
FOUNDATION
ENGINEERING

BY

WEST'S PILING & CONSTRUCTION
COMPANY LIMITED

BATH ROAD, HARMONDSWORTH
WEST DRAYTON, MIDDLESEX

TEL : WEST DRAYTON 2288 (5 lines)
AFTER MAY 1958—SKYPORT 5222 (9 lines)

LONDON OFFICE: Columbia House, Aldwych, London, W.C.2.   *Tel: Holborn 4108*
NORTHERN OFFICE: Albion Ironworks, Manchester, 10.   *Tel: Collyhurst 3049*
SCOTTISH OFFICE: 169 Hamilton Road, Glasgow, E.2.   *Tel: Shettleston 2927*

ASSOCIATED AUSTRALASIAN COMPANY:
West's Shell Piling (A/sia) Pty Ltd, Melbourne and Sydney

LICENSEES:
Ireland : Farrans Limited, Dunmurry, Belfast
Continent : Compagnie Générale de Construction de Fours, 8 place des États-Unis, Paris

Published by
West's Piling & Construction Co. Ltd
March, 1957
Reprinted December, 1957

FRANK WEST

W. A. VALON

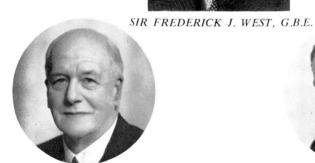

SIR FREDERICK J. WEST, G.B.E.

ERNEST WEST

JOHN F. WEST

A. G. BIRD

CONTENTS

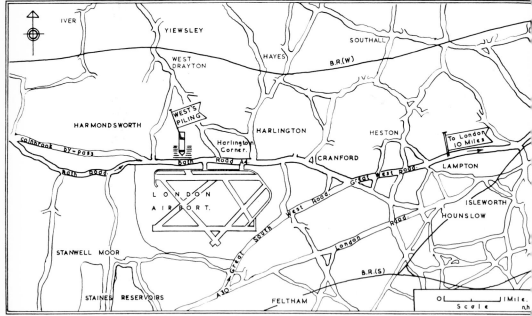

Location map showing situation of West's Piling & Construction Co. Ltd

Aerial view of the Company's Head Office and Works at Harmondsworth

Contracts Described
in Chapter Four

Head Office, West's Piling & Construction Company Limited

PREFACE

THE demand for our " Published References " from many branches of industry, from technical colleges and training centres, has been so gratifying that we make no apology for presenting another book on the work of West's Piling & Construction Company. Here, without attempting a complete treatise on the subject, we have expanded those sections of the previous book which deal generally with the problems involved in foundation work. More complete information is available in extant literature and a list of the more recent works is given at the end of the relevant chapters.

A sure foundation is an essential requirement in the erection of any type of building, and the modern tendency to erect increasingly heavy structures on restricted sites, often containing sub-strata unsuitable for heavy load bearing, has led to a considerable expansion in the use of piled foundations.

In the comparison between the two principal types of concrete piles, the precast and the cast-in-situ, much ingenuity has been shown in the attempt to combine the advantages of both.

The West's Shell Pile achieves this desirable combination in a particularly happy manner.

A reinforced concrete tube in prefabricated sections is built up section by section on a mandrel and, preceded by a solid concrete shoe, is driven into the ground until a predetermined driving set is reached.

The driving mandrel is then withdrawn and the hollow pile may be inspected internally prior to the casting in place of the reinforced concrete core. Thus a visual assurance of soundness is added to the advantage achieved by the definite dynamic set.

Since the appearance of " Published References ", confidence has been maintained in this system with its direct evidence of stability enabling structures of great concentrated weight, further examples of which are included in the following pages, to be supported on foundations whose essential element is the West's Shell Pile.

A. G. Bird

M.I.Mech.E., M.Inst.Gas E.

11

CHAPTER ONE

THE SOIL MECHANICS OF PILING

THE part of the earth's crust with which the civil engineer is generally concerned consists of two kinds of material differentiated by the terms " rock " and " soil ". There are several intermediate grades, such as heavily weathered or decomposed rocks and strongly compacted soils, but the line of demarcation is sufficiently accurate to allow these general terms to apply to all materials upon which foundations are likely to be based.

Rocks are classified as igneous, sedimentary or metamorphic. They are all natural aggregates of mineral grains connected by strong and permanent cohesive forces. The igneous rocks, e.g. granite and basalt, form the permanent earth structure, resulting from the cooling of the original " molten mass ". Their solidity is such that they usually do not give rise to any problems when used as a foundation base. Sedimentary rocks, e.g. limestones, dolomites, shale and sandstones, are the products of physical deposition or chemical decomposition, generally solidified by pressure of the overburden and therefore often laminated in structure. They may decompose rapidly under atmospheric conditions and may have many fissures and faults ; careful examination is therefore sometimes necessary before basing foundations upon them. Metamorphic rocks, e.g. schist, slate and quartzite, have been produced by the action of heat and/or pressure on igneous and sedimentary rocks and can therefore have the characteristics of either ; they can usually be regarded as a satisfactory base for foundation structures. All rock formations may contain zones of weakness but generally they are at least as strong as the concrete foundation which may be built upon them.

The maximum safe load-bearing capacities of rocks vary from 100 tons per square foot for such igneous rocks as granite to 6 tons for a good quality sedimentary rock such as hard solid chalk. Sedimentary rocks, however, may be thinly bedded or extensively shattered in which case they have bearing values below 6 tons per square foot ; in these cases, careful preliminary examination is necessary. Within the limits of practical loading, rock may be treated as an elastic material, obeying Hooke's law of proportionality of deformation to load, a useful point in the calculation of settlement.

Soil, originally produced by the disintegration of rock portions of the earth's crust, is defined as a natural aggregate of mineral grains with or without organic constituents, that can be separated by gentle mechanical means, such as agitation in water. The principal terms used by civil engineers to describe soils are, gravel, sand, silt and clay. Careful soil analysis is usually desirable to ascertain the properties of these strata if any one is to be considered as a bearing for a foundation. The category into which a soil is placed is determined by the particle size of the material. Often sub-strata consist of an admixture of soils or contain organic substances such as peat. By far the most complex of all soils to the foundation engineer is clay, as it is so often applied to strata loosely and in general terms. Soils are sometimes split into two categories : (a) coarse-grained gravel and sand, whose non-cohesive particles are visible to the naked eye, and (b) fine grained silt and clay, whose particles are generally cohesive and not visible to the naked eye. Finally, there is the top soil which is mainly organic and consists of partially decomposed vegetable matter.

Gravel generally occurs as sediment from flowing water or, if at a reasonable depth, from ice, particularly in the accumulated deposits of the Ice Age, the latter types occurring in " loess " or " till " (boulder clay). Gravel can consist of the debris of a large variety of rocks and is designated " pit ", " sea ", " river ", " glacial ", according to the manner of its origin and formation. What is more important to the foundation engineer is the degree of compactness or density of the formation. It is therefore of value to undertake penetration tests to determine the possible depth or rate of penetration of piles.

Sand is distinguished from gravel, with which it is often mixed, by the much smaller maximum particle size. Its degree of compactness varies considerably with a consequent variation in resistance to pile-driving. It is liable to be saturated with water and when it occurs in the form of " running sand " it presents acute foundation problems.

Silt can be either organic or inorganic, the former being a sedimentary deposit from weathered material and the latter having settled from water as a final deposition. All types of silts are, however, dangerous for foundations, as they are subject to considerable " flow " under pressure and their characteristics change with the varying water content.

Clays are essentially colloidal deposits with water, formed as a sediment from the decomposition of minerals, such as felspar and mica, their particle size and water content varying considerably. Clays are classified geologically under four main headings :

1. Boulder clay, a glacial formation containing large fragments of rock torn from the parent material by ice movements.
2. Loess, originally used to describe a particular type of alluvial sediment found in the Rhine Valley. Loess now covers a range of siliceous materials produced either from glacial formations or as a wind-borne

dust found in arid regions and compacted under pressure. It may assume considerable compactness when deposited in thick layers.

3. China clays (and laterite), formed by the weathering of certain mineral silicates.

4. Sedimentary clays, mainly river-borne sediment (see 2).

The first three types may occur in strata of considerable thickness. They are normally compact and have a reasonably high bearing value. The sedimentary clays, however, have an entirely different composition and their characteristics vary with the conditions of their deposition and present state. These clays are normally fissured as opposed to the other types of clay which are sensibly homogeneous and uniform in structure.

Clays are not "inert"; they are essentially plastic and can "flow" under pressure. The natural water content of clay varies from 15 to 40 per cent.; clay is considered to be in a plastic state when the water content exceeds 22 per cent. Clay strata, therefore, which are to be involved in the construction of foundations need to be carefully analysed with consideration of the fact that their water content may vary not only with pressure but also with weather conditions. Particular attention must be paid to the possibility of these variations in connection with the settlement of foundations.

A comparatively recent phenomenon is "made ground" upon which many buildings have been erected. Made ground can often be called upon to withstand a small load but this can only safely be permitted after stringent investigations have been carried out not only on the filled material itself but also on the underlying strata.

The maximum safe load-bearing capacities for soils range from 6 tons per square foot for compact sand and gravel and stiff boulder clay down to $\frac{1}{2}$ ton per square foot for loose sand and soft clays.

FOUNDATIONS

The object of the foundation upon which any given structure is to be built is to transmit the weight of the structure to one of the underlying strata of the earth's crust which is sufficiently compact and permanent to withstand the load about to be superimposed upon it, either with no subsidence or only such subsidence as will be non-injurious to the structure. The modern tendency to concentrate weight per unit area, seen to the extreme in the "skyscraper", calls for increasing care and skill in deciding upon the type and design of the foundation. The difficulty is further increased by the growing necessity, arising from space and economic considerations, to utilize ground which would, a few years ago, have been deemed totally unfit for building upon. Hence the knowledge of soil mechanics and the experience of the foundation engineer and contractor becomes of greater value to a widening range of architects and clients.

Engineers deciding upon the type of foundation for any particular

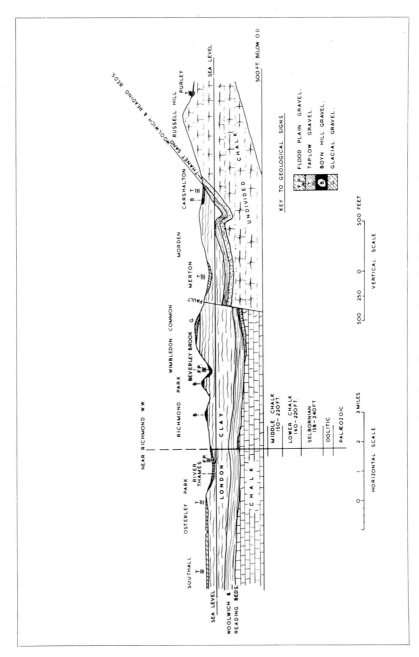

Fig. 1. *Typical geological section through the Thames Valley*

16

structure must consider a number of factors : (*a*) the function of the structure; (*b*) the nature, and disposition, of the loads to be supported ; (*c*) the condition and nature of the subsoil ; (*d*) the necessity to keep the cost of foundations relative to that of the structure within economic limits.

The function of the structure and its loads are dictated by the client but the foundation engineer often influences both these factors, sometimes to the extent of advising a re-design of the sub-structure when foundations may become excessively costly, particularly where piling is required. The subsoil conditions must be investigated and the more detailed the investigations are, the more accurate is the estimate of cost. Cost is becoming of increasing significance and is often the determining factor in the selection of foundation design.

It has been authoritatively stated that the only sound and well-defined rule in favour of a piled foundation is that it shall be economically unsound to use ordinary methods of direct bearing on the soil. There are, however, other factors which influence the decision : speed of construction, safety to men and property, construction in or through water. For instance, piling may be necessary, even if apparently at greater cost, to avoid deep excavations which would disturb the bearing strata of adjacent buildings. The advantages of piling are most marked on reclaimed land (Southampton New Docks), filled areas (Avonmouth), and estuarine flats (Thames Valley —a geological section is reproduced in Fig. 1), all areas popular as sites for jetties, warehouses, heavy industry and power stations.

The purpose of calculating the strength of load-bearing strata is to determine their resistance both to ultimate failure and to detrimental settlement, whether of piled or direct-bearing foundations. To ensure against ultimate failure, the safe working load should be limited to a value varying between one-half and one-third of the ultimate failure load according to the nature of the load and the accuracy of the information available. Test loading gives more positive and accurate information—and thus it is normally sufficient to load a pile or the stratum on which a direct bearing is anticipated to 1·5 times its maximum working load. Settlement if controlled is not always detrimental. The allowable settlement is determined by the function and type of structure supported. In general, settlement greater than, say, $\frac{3}{4}$ in. should be avoided. Differential settlement must be avoided in all circumstances, since it may lead to serious distortion and damage to the structure.

As above stated, rock and gravel (ballast) generally provide satisfactory bearing strata and the type of foundation selected is determined by economic considerations arising out of their depth below the surface and the constructional problems involved. Top soil, organic deposits and (normally) filled materials are excavated or piles are driven through them to a more stable stratum below. Discussion of the load-bearing properties of strata may therefore be limited to foundations in sand, silt and clay.

The suitability of sand as a load-bearing stratum depends on its density and the position of the water table. Both have an appreciable effect on bearing capacity and settlement. The situation of the water table, which may vary seasonally as well as by subsequent drainage, is a most important factor in construction cost. The width of the footing and the depth of surcharge on the footing are calculated to give a factor of safety of 3 on the ultimate bearing capacity of the stratum. If the width of the footing thus calculated is excessive, piling is adopted. The settlement is deduced from the unit weight (density) of the sand, consideration being given to the fact that settlement will be aggravated by a rise in the level of the water table. In " running sand " piling is also to be recommended. Piles driven into sand develop their resistance partly from end-bearing and partly from skin friction, the proportion varying with the density of the sand. Piling is also adopted where a bearing is required to be established below the scour of moving water. A useful advantage of piling in sand is that the driven piles " compact " loose sand and increase its bearing capacity by increasing skin friction.

Silts can be plastic, with the characteristics of clay, or non-plastic, akin to sand. They are often treated as sand in the consideration of foundation problems. Loess, if unsaturated, is capable of withstanding loads of several tons per square foot but breaks down to a silt if saturated. If footings in silt are to be considered, a loading test, under true working conditions, should be carried out on the undisturbed stratum. In the majority of cases piling is preferable. Silt has an appreciable frictional value ; the driving of the pile " liquefies " the silt, making driving easy, but the friction returns within a few days and sometimes exceeds the bearing value of the original material. Load tests, only, can determine the ultimate bearing value with any accuracy.

The load-bearing capacity of clay depends on its resistance to shear, usually one-half its unconfined compressive strength. Settlement depends on its compressibility. Both values can be determined in the laboratory although field tests are advisable before coming to final conclusions. In calculating bearing capacity, a factor of safety of 3 is necessary against ultimate failure. Footings should be sufficiently far apart so that the combination of all loads when spread at 60° from the edges of the footings does not over-stress the clay at lower depths. If the strength of the clay deteriorates with depth, footings are less safe and piling may be necessary. Settlement, especially differential settlement, may result from the changing and irregular water content of clays. Generally, therefore, if the clay is too soft or too compressible for footings or a raft, the weight of the structure should be transferred to piles relying either on end-bearing or friction.

PILES AND PILING

Most systems of piling fall into two main categories : (a) the precast pile, sometimes prestressed, and (b) the cast-in-situ pile, driven or bored.

18

The West's Shell Pile falls into neither of these categories; it is rather a combination of both types, having, as will be seen later, the advantages of both. The choice of type of pile, other than on economic grounds, is governed largely by site conditions.

Precast piles may be made on the site or in a factory and transported to the site. In either case, in addition to being of strength capable of sustaining the load to be borne and the stresses set up in driving, they must possess sufficient strength to withstand the considerable stresses set up in handling and transport. These stresses, in a long pile, may be so considerable as to exceed the useful load-bearing capacity of the pile. Precast piles have a uniform section and can be inspected before, but not after, driving. They have the disadvantage of being heavy and cumbersome, both in the pile itself and in the machinery and equipment required to handle and drive the pile, and the driving of long piles is slow and costly. With the exception of the prestressed concrete pile, a greater amount of steel reinforcement is required than for the cast-in-situ or the West's Shell Pile. But probably the main disadvantage of the precast pile is that its required length cannot be accurately known before driving. If it is found to be too long, unnecessary expenditure has been incurred and the surplus length must be cut away. If too short, the pile must be stripped and lengthened in-situ and the piling frame returned to re-drive the pile—a costly procedure.

The bored-in-situ pile is constructed by sinking a shoeless tube, removing the core of soil within it and placing the concrete and steel reinforcement in the hole thus made while withdrawing the tube. With the driven-in-situ pile a steel tube with a shoe is driven into the ground with a heavy hammer, the soil being displaced. The tube is filled with concrete, either rammed or under pressure, and withdrawn in stages. Bored piles cause little vibration and can be used on difficult sites and in limited headroom. They also indicate the type of soil in which the pile is to rest. They can also be used to penetrate tipped materials and densely packed sand or gravel. The main disadvantages of the cast-in-situ piles are that they do not have a uniform cross-section, they cannot be inspected either before or after casting, and the new, uncured concrete can be disturbed by adjacent piling and such other causes as soil or water movements occurring before the concrete has set. Particularly, they are not safe when cast in very soft ground. They rely very much on the standard of site workmanship and only a test load can determine their safe bearing capacity.

REFERENCES

Lake & Rastall's Textbook of Geology. Fifth edition.
London, Edward Arnold & Co. (490 pages.)

Soil Mechanics in Engineering Practice, by Terzaghi & Peck.
Third edition. London, Chapman & Hall Ltd. (560 pages.)

The Mechanics of Engineering Soils, by Capper & Cassie.
Second edition. London, E. & F. N. Spon Ltd. (310 pages.)

CHAPTER TWO

THE WEST'S SHELL PILE

MUCH ingenuity has been displayed in devising means of securing the advantages of the in-situ pile, while retaining the element of certainty in the precast pile which itself has actually been driven to a set. One successful development is the West's Shell Pile of which many hundred linear miles of pile length have been used. It is shown diagrammatically in Figs. 2 and 3. A reinforced concrete tube in prefabricated sections is threaded on to a mandrel and assembled upon a solid concrete driving shoe. The whole of the tube, mandrel and shoe is driven, new sections being added as required, until the calculated predetermined set is obtained, when the steel mandrel is withdrawn, leaving the shoe and tube in the position to which they have been actually driven to the required set. A cage of reinforcement is then suspended in the concrete tube and concrete is poured in, forming an unstressed solid core. It should here be noted that a light can be lowered within the tube for inspection purposes before filling. Where corrosive water is present in the subsoil, the shells and shoe are made with acid-resisting cement, thus forming a protective skin around the pile.

In the driving of this shell pile the energy of the falling hammer is transmitted to the mandrel and shells by way of the composite driving head shown in Fig. 4. The hammer actually strikes a timber dolly encased in a steel helmet located loosely in the top of the driving head, and the force of the blow is transmitted to the mandrel-driving section which is rigidly fixed to the mandrels. As the mandrels pass through the full length of the pile shells and are in contact with the shoe, the force on the mandrel is applied direct to the shoe. Around the lower portion of the mandrel-driving section of the head and fixed to it by vertical bolts through circular horizontal flanges is the shell-driving section in two separate parts. The distance of the upper part from the flange of the mandrel-driving section is controlled by a number of plain washers on the vertical bolts; the proportion of the blow to be transmitted to the shells is regulated by varying this distance. Between the upper and lower sections of the shell-driving section are several nests of Belleville disc spring washers located by the vertical bolts, thus cushioning the effective blow directed to the shells. The proportion of the driving

20

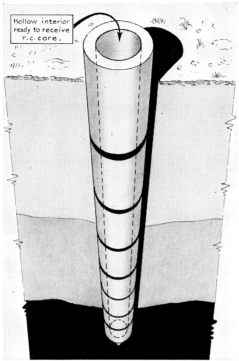

Hollow interior ready to receive r.c. core.

Fig. 2
A West's Shell Pile driven to set and awaiting the placing of the cast-in-situ core.

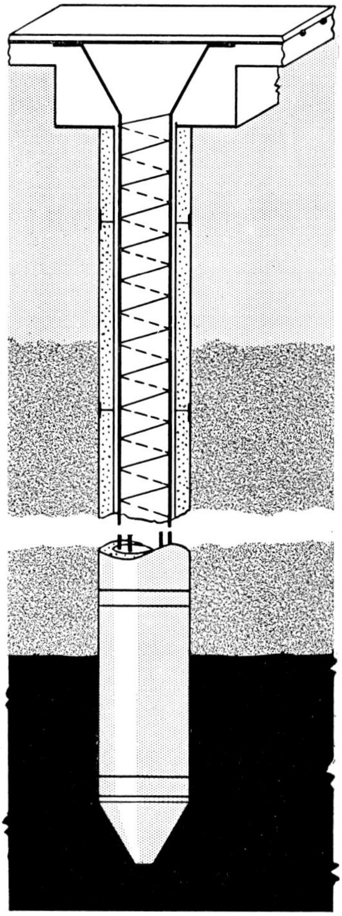

Fig. 3
A completed West's Shell Pile (in part section) with pilecap.

Fig. 4
Driving head for West's Shell Piles.

21

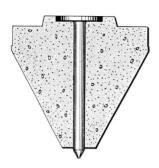

Fig. 5
Reinforced pile shoe for
hard driving.

Fig. 6   A West's mobile diesel piling
outfit suitable for undulating sites.

Fig. 7
A lorry-mounted
mobile petrol-diesel
piling outfit.

force to be transmitted to the shells is determined by the amount of skin friction encountered in the strata to be penetrated.

When heavy driving is necessary, a specially reinforced shoe is used with a steel disc presented to the toe of the driving mandrel, and a steel point projecting ahead of the shoe to make the initial penetration of the hard stratum (Fig. 5).

PILE-DRIVING MACHINES

Fig. 6 is an example of a machine constructed from the base of mechanical excavators powered by diesel engines of 70 to 87 h.p. The total weight is 25–30 tons, but being self-propelled on tracks it can be used on undulating sites with a comparatively poor bearing surface. For the leaders a headroom of 37 ft 6 in. is required and the hammer weight is 3 to 4 tons ; it is capable of driving shell piles to a depth of 120 ft. This type of machine is probably the most mobile and convenient so far devised. When the driving of one pile is complete the machine travels rapidly under its own power to the position of the next. The erection and dismantling of the machine is simple and quick, and it can commence piling operations within a few hours of its arrival on the site.

A machine mounted on wheels is shown in Fig. 7. It is constructed upon an ex-Army tractor-lorry of about 10 tons capacity, powered by a 48-h.p. petrol engine, which, by means of three differential gears, can be arranged to drive all the 10 wheels if necessary. The piling winch mounted on the lorry is powered by a 30-h.p. diesel engine, and the total weight is just over 10 tons. The whole apparatus can be driven by road to the site, but its use is limited to reasonably level ground with a fairly good bearing surface. For the leaders, a headroom of 28 ft is required and the hammer weight is 2 to 3 tons.

PILING CALCULATIONS

The bearing capacity of the precast or any positively driven pile, such as the West's Shell Pile, is capable of definite mathematical treatment, for which purpose the " Hiley Formula " is appropriate :

$$S + \frac{C}{2} = \frac{W.h}{R} \times \frac{W + Pe^2}{W + P}$$

where
- S = final set in inches.
- C = total temporary compression.
- W = weight of hammer.
- h = drop of hammer.
- R = driving resistance.
- P = weight of pile and mandrel.
- e = coefficient of restitution (cast-iron to wood).

23

The total temporary compression " C " is the sum of the compression of the ground and dolly or " quake " (C_1) and the compression of the pile and mandrel (C_2).

In practice " C " may be measured by a simple form of set recorder consisting of a board covered with drawing paper rigidly attached to the pile and a straight edge adjacent to the paper but supported on fixed points. During the period whilst the hammer is striking the pile a pencil is drawn along the straight edge and this records the actual movement of the pile on the drawing paper.

C_2 is deduced from the formula :

$$\frac{\text{Stress}}{\text{Strain}} = E$$

The resistance to penetration (R) is taken as the working load (L) multiplied by the factor of safety (3), and an equivalent cross-sectional area of the pile (A) is calculated on the assumption that E (Concrete) : E (Steel) = 1 : 12, and the formula therefore resolves into :

$$C_2 = \frac{R}{E} \times \frac{L}{A}$$

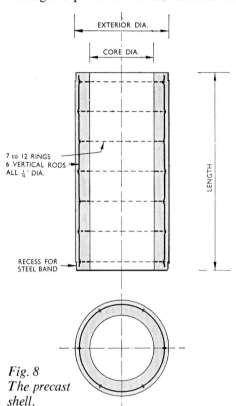

Fig. 8
The precast shell.

See schedule on page 26

C_1 is therefore obtained by deducting C_2 from the total C as measured ; from past experiments carried out in many instances, this approximates to ·001 R. This approximation has been found to be particularly applicable at the time the set is reached, that is, when the resistance to penetration is of a fairly high order.

The Hiley Formula, in common with most equations regarding the bearing capacity of piles, is derived from dynamic principles, that is, from the equations for the collision of elastic bodies, and the coefficient of restitution " e " is a figure which depends on the nature and shape of the two materials which are involved in the impact of the hammer upon the driving head of the pile. The value which experience has shown to correspond most closely to the average conditions obtaining in the " West's Piling " system is 0·32.

A typical application of the formula is as follows :

Type of outfit	Mobile—Long Mandrels
Working load of pile . . .	L = 60 tons
Factor of safety	= 3
Driving resistance . . .	R = 3 × L = 180 tons
Weight of hammer . . .	W = 3 tons
Drop of hammer	h = 33 in.
Diameter of pile	= $17\frac{1}{2}$ in.
Length of pile	l = 30 ft
Weight of pile and mandrel . .	P = 3·55 tons
Coefficient of restitution—cast-iron to wood : assume	e = 0·32
Temporary compression of dolly and ground (from past experiments)	C_1 = ·001 R = ·180 in.
Temporary compression of pile .	C_2 = ·173 in.
Total temporary compression .	C = $C_1 + C_2$ = ·353 in.

Then, according to Hiley Formula

$$S + \frac{C}{2} = \frac{W.h}{R} \times \frac{W + Pe^2}{W + P}$$

$$S + \frac{C}{2} = \frac{3 \times 33}{180} \times \frac{3 + (3·55 \times ·32^2)}{3 + 3·55}$$

$$= \frac{99}{180} \times \frac{3·36}{6·55}$$

$$= ·282 \text{ in.}$$

S = 0·282 — 0·177 = ·105 in., i.e. 10 blows to last inch.

TYPES OF SHELL PILES

The West's Shell Pile is stocked in three sizes each consisting of standard reinforced concrete increments of tubular section as indicated in Fig. 8. The outer diameter of the R.C. Shell varies from $14\frac{1}{2}$ in. to 20 in., the core diameter and steel reinforcement also varying proportionately as shown in the schedule on the next page.

Maximum loads for the various sizes of pile have been tabulated but a small range is necessary for this figure depending on the depth at which the load-bearing stratum is encountered and also the various types of strata which have to be driven through in order to reach the desired resistance to penetration.

The optimum size of pile to be used is decided in each individual case after consideration of the available site particulars and the type of structure to be supported.

SCHEDULE

Exterior diameter	Core diameter	Shell length	Maximum load
20″	15″	3′– 0″	70–100т
17½″	12″	3′– 0″	50 – 60т
14½″	10⅞″	4′– 0″	30 – 40т

SHELL MANUFACTURE AND CONCRETE CONTROL

Concrete control plays a basic part in the manufacture of the concrete shells, as it does for all high quality precast concrete products. A few notes on this subject, therefore, might be of interest.

The Civil Engineer, the Structural Engineer and the Architect, directly and indirectly between them incorporate over 10,000,000 tons of cement annually in concretes. A very large proportion of this cement is used as an engineering material, in the form of reinforced concrete, to resist a series of predetermined loads that have been carefully calculated. It is, therefore, not surprising that considerable interest has developed in the field of concrete technology because of the urgent need of the engineer to work with materials of particular and well-defined properties if he is to build soundly and economically.

It is extremely rare that a cement intended to comply with B.S. 12 will fail to do so and although cements of the same type do vary considerably as between works, deliveries are reasonably consistent from any one source. The chief cause of variation in concrete is usually centred on the batching and mixing plant.

There are many contributory causes of variation; those enumerated below are, however, of major importance.

1. Although certain aspects of concreting are certainly skilled operations, the building and civil engineering industries and trade unions connected therewith have never recognized a craft of concreter. Thus the batching and mixing of concrete, which is a fairly precise chemical engineering process, is usually left in the hands of unskilled labour.

2. On many sites and even in precast yards, little or no check is kept

upon the qualities of the coarse and fine aggregates purchased. Because of this, aggregates having wide grading variations and perhaps contaminated with dirt and silt are used in the concrete, to its detriment.

3. Because the addition of water is one of the easiest ways of increasing the workability of concrete, this device is used rather than the more skilled method of adjusting the coarse to fine ratio of the aggregates. This somewhat indiscriminate use of water causes large variations in the strength, density and moisture movement or shrinkage of the concrete.

4. On many sites the coarse and fine aggregates are dumped too close to one another with no separating barrier to prevent each from contaminating the other. Because of this it is not possible to ensure that all the batches made are of the correct proportions and hence both workability and strength are affected.

Having commented generally upon the principal causes of variation in concrete quality some notes on mixing concrete may be of value. In the first place the weigh-batcher, which should always be used in preference to volume batching, and the mixer should be checked for performance—the weigh-batcher for accuracy over its range of operation and the mixer to ensure that it is correctly set up as to level and height of discharge. The apparatus for measuring the water into the mixing drum should be checked over a few deliveries, say three, and any adjustment necessary to ensure correct measurement should be made. Once a mix is being made the drum speed of the mixer should be determined (revs. per minute) and compared with the makers' recommended speed, adjustment being made accordingly. After a period of mixing of 1·5 to 2·0 minutes the mixer should be stopped and the mix examined in the drum to check by eye that segregation of the ingredients is not taking place. There is a tendency in fixed horizontal drum mixers to throw the water either to the back or the front of the mix. This is particularly noticeable when a low water content concrete is being made for vibration placing ; in these mixes the water content is sufficiently low to make a poor distribution throughout the mix easily discernible. This fault can be corrected quite frequently by tipping the mixer so that the water tends to gravitate to the opposite side of the drum.

Any concrete which is to be placed by vibration should appear harsh and under-sanded when first discharged from the mixer. Such a concrete if of the correct proportions will compact easily and rapidly under the influence of a modern high frequency internal vibrator. The compacted concrete will be very firm, dense and of maximum strength for the particular water/cement ratio employed. On the other hand if the mix as discharged can be easily worked up to a good finish with two or three strokes of a trowel, then it may be assumed that segregation will start to develop as soon as the vibrator is applied to it.

West's Piling & Construction Company, with their ever-expanding use of concrete for civil engineering works and in particular in the formation of pile shells and finished piles, have appreciated the importance of having expert advice available on the many problems involved in concrete technology. The shells are manufactured with factory precision and control, being specially designed to withstand handling and driving stresses as well as those stresses imposed by direct or indirect loading. For some time now, on all major works, a complete investigation has been made into the available aggregates and suitable mixes are designed to meet the particular site and driving conditions; in consequence much time and some anxiety are saved in the initial stages of a contract because it is known before concreting starts that the material to be used will place properly and develop the desired qualities of strength, density and resistance to chemical and other attack. Nevertheless, in order to be assured that the initial high quality of the concrete is maintained, constant checks are made on the making and placing of the concrete by tests at regular intervals on standard 6 in. cubes which are sent to an independent testing authority for report on their densities and compressive strengths.

THE ADVANTAGES OF THE SHELL PILE

West's Shell Pile is a unit of sound engineering construction. It can be designed with confidence to suit many and varied subsoil conditions and combinations of loading. Additional steel reinforcement can be placed in the top of the pile to resist bending stresses or horizontal forces. As the steel is placed after the pile has been driven, West's Shell Pile can cater for last-minute revisions in the loading—a feature not possible in the precast pile

The pile is always driven to the correct dynamic set, to the depth required by this set and no further. Thus stability is ensured. The bearing capacity of each pile can be calculated, but, of equal importance, the proportion between the toe resistance and skin friction can be ascertained. This feature is unique in West's Shell Pile and is worthy of further discussion. The pile is driven in the normal way until the required set is reached and the total bearing capacity is calculated. The driving head is then disconnected from the top shell and a set is taken on the shoe only; the toe resistance is thus obtained. The difference between the two figures evaluates the skin friction developed between the pile and the surrounding soils. These three values can be determined—provided the soil is not too soft—at any depth, thus yielding valuable information of practical importance.

As West's Shell Pile can be driven from almost any level and its core filled to, and finished at, any depth (e.g. at the designed finished level of the pile), there is no waste of material. The pile shells finish at or below ground level and the expensive " graveyard " effect of excess-length precast piles is never seen on a West's piling site. Cutting of pile heads is reduced to the

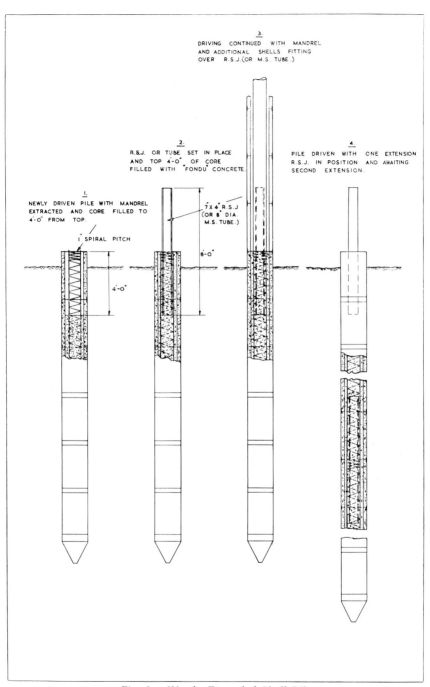

Fig. 9. West's Extended Shell Pile

29

minimum since only the top shell, which may be protruding after the set is reached, needs to be cut and the pile core trimmed. West's Shell Pile can readily be extended above ground level, by placing and coring additional shells, or by building up the pile inside a steel collar (see Poole, p. 65). The pile is thus often used as a column in basements, jetties and similar structures.

A fascinating and unique feature of West's Shell Pile is that the interior can be inspected from top to bottom after driving and before concreting the core. There is no risk of variation in cross-section because the shells are precast and are subjected to the usual rigid tests carried out on all precast concrete products of high standard. The core concrete is never contaminated by impurities in the subsoil because it is protected by the precast shell. The shell can be cast in ciment-fondu or sulphate-resisting cement while the core may be filled with ordinary Portland cement concrete. The pile core suffers no fatigue since it is cast in-situ after driving is completed. The concrete mixture and the steel reinforcement can be varied to suit loading conditions.

There is less vibration and noise in driving than with any other form of driven pile. As the majority of the impact is transmitted to the toe of the pile, danger to adjacent foundations and surrounding property is reduced to the minimum.

Special mobile piling plants, supported by a large modern fleet of Bedford trucks and trailers and a large stock of matured shells maintained at the Works, enable piling to commence immediately and to proceed with the utmost speed. Extensive site preparation before driving is rendered unnecessary. This specially designed plant has enabled West's Shell Piles to be driven under many and varied site conditions.

An appreciable demand has arisen for very long piles, and engineers had been forced to specify the steel box pile. To meet this demand, West's Piling & Construction Company have developed an adaptation of the standard pile known as " West's Extended Shell Pile ". With this technique, piles up to 120 ft in length can be driven. The pile is driven in two or three stages, the number and length of the stages being determined by the condition of the subsoil strata through which the pile is to be driven. The first section of the pile is driven in the normal manner and the core is concreted to within 4 feet of the top of the driven shell. When the core has set, an 8 ft long 7 in. $\times$ 4 in. rolled steel joist or 8 in. dia. steel tube is embedded in ciment-fondu and inserted in the core (see Fig. 9). A specially designed steel mandrel is threaded over the joist and further shells are fixed. The solid shell section, with the empty shells above, is now re-driven to the required set or through the next stage. The process can be repeated once again. The presence of the stiffening member adds materially to the strength of the pile so that a reduction can be made in its effective length and in the area of the main steel reinforcement. Alternatively, the working load may often be increased.

30

For this reason and many others (e.g. the pile can be designed specifically for any individual site or loading conditions) West's Shell Pile can carry more load per unit area than any other system.

REFERENCES

The Resistance of Piles to Penetration, by R. V. Allin. Second edition. London, E. & F. N. Spon Ltd. (125 pages).

Piling for Foundations, by R. R. Minikin. London, Crosby Lockwood & Son Ltd. (190 pages.)

CHAPTER THREE

SOME FOUNDATION PROBLEMS

THE factors to be considered in determining the type of foundation most suited to the specific loading and subsoil conditions have already been indicated briefly. If, after having studied and interpreted the available data, particularly from their practical aspects, it is decided to design for a foundation bearing directly on the soil at a comparatively shallow depth, then three main types of structures are presented : the strip footing, the raft (solid or cellular) and the base and pier foundation.

The strip footing, used in such structures as houses, schools and light factories, is founded as near the surface as practical—consistent with the intensity of loading. Special consideration is given, in determining the depth of strip footings, to the following :

(a) Seasonal changes and the possibility of the lowering and rising of the water table.

(b) Removal of lateral support causing undermining and seepage of the soil supporting the footing.

(c) Drying out of silts and clays causing shrinkage. This shrinkage can be produced by many and varied causes, both man-made and natural in origin. Sudden climatic changes or the extraction of water from the clay by adjacent poplar trees, temperature changes in boiler-house basements or the phenomenon of " artificial freezing " of the soils all alter the water content of clays quite considerably. All such causes have resulted in serious failures in the past.

(d) Disturbance due to vibration and future construction.

With strip footings it is advisable to arrange for the pressure per unit area to vary only between very close limits. This is done by adjusting the width and/or depth of the concrete base. If it is impracticable to obtain such a balance, a flexible footing is used—or a raft foundation. Strip footings are commonly used to support and distribute pressures caused by uniformly distributed line loads, as produced by load-bearing walls, or by columns of a building that are closely spaced in one direction.

Where the loading is uniform over a large area, such as for a gasholder foundation, or where the column supports are closely spaced in both directions, a raft foundation is often adopted. With high point loads transferred

32

to soils of low bearing capacities the extent of the independent bases may almost cover the space between the columns carrying the loads. In this case also a raft would prove economical. Solid rafts, whatever their type or shape, are usually designed as reinforced concrete flat slabs ; being thickened where the intensity of loading exceeds the average uniformly distributed load on the main body of the raft. Loads are thus spread over the whole area of the raft. As it is not practicable, and sometimes impossible, to determine with any degree of accuracy the moments and shear forces caused by differential settlement, the raft is reinforced more heavily than as calculated to allow for this, thus ensuring that the slab will span over any small hollows caused by uneven settlement of the ground. If the structures are required to be constructed over highly compressible strata, then the cellular raft may be adopted. This consists of top and bottom reinforced concrete slabs braced with intermediate ribs. Its depth is often determined so that the weight of the raft and the structure to be supported is wholly compensated by the weight of the excavated soil. Thus the settlement of the structure becomes negligible. This type of structure is often referred to as a " floating " raft as it is kept in stable equilibrium by the balancing of the total downward and upward pressures. Any one section of the ground is prevented from being overstressed as the raft is designed to be stiff enough to transfer excess load from the weaker section to a more compact section of the material upon which the structure is based.

A base and pier foundation is often used when the depth of a satisfactory bearing stratum occurs between 5 ft and 10 ft below the surface—for at these depths neither a raft foundation, nor a piled foundation may be found to be economical. If a basement or pit is required, the principles of the cellular raft may be adopted. The base and pier design allows for the weight of the structure to be carried down through a pier or column of concrete, brick, etc. to a reinforced concrete pad—the load being spread over an area sufficient to reduce the maximum pressure on the bearing strata to that permissible. The base and pier foundation often brings many constructional problems such as timbering, pumping, etc. and piles may be substituted even if only driven to a comparatively shallow depth.

It is not easy to reach a decision in the selection of the right type of foundation for a specific structure. Many conditions, other than financial, influence such a decision. A few examples taken at random from the Company's records will show how various foundations have been selected and how the design and constructional problems have been overcome. It is hoped that these examples, together with those in Chapter 4, will indicate the versatility and variety of experience that West's Piling & Construction Company have accumulated during thirty-two years' existence.

A variety of types of foundation design were used at Stapleton Road Gasworks, Bristol, in several contracts for the South-Western Gas Board. The retort house was built on hard shale whose depth varied between 5 ft and 10 ft from the surface. It was possible here to have a very simple form of combined mass and reinforced concrete block structure tied together with a stiff concrete floor slab. In the spaces between the blocks the conveyor tunnels were formed with a sub-basement as the firing floor. For the purification and sulphur treatment plant a combination of piled and pier foundations was used to support the main structure, which was entirely of reinforced concrete. This design was necessitated by variations in the shale stratum and the complexity of the sub-structure. Ancillary buildings were placed on strip foundations on a clay stratum about 2 ft 6 in. below the surface, whilst light plant, external to the buildings, were supported on rafts.

The supporting of a tar and liquor tank at Reading Gasworks also presented a complexity of problems due mainly to the existence of two concrete slabs, one at a depth of 5 ft, the other some 10 ft below the surface. Extensive site investigation was carried out with the result that the final design accommodated four different types of support for the new foundation slab. The first part of the slab was supported on piles driven through the upper subterranean concrete base down to ballast; the second on piles, with flat bulbous shoes, resting on the lower base; the third on piles driven directly in the ballast; the fourth on piers built upon a heavy concrete block some 4 ft below the surface. No settlement has been recorded.

At Newcastle, the beam-raft principle was adopted. Here the whole retort house, settings and plant, were carried on a lattice-work frame of reinforced concrete beams supported on compact sand. This foundation was not as simple as it first appeared as loose particles of sand in some areas necessitated a considerable amount of special design. In parts, a most complicated beam structure was required so that the loose sand pockets were spanned—allowing the loading above them to be distributed to beams supported on good ground.

A type of cellular raft foundation was designed and constructed to support a series of silos for Messrs Cadbury Brothers at Frampton. A reasonably compact but irregular ballast stratum, overlying the natural chalk, was found at some 6 ft below the surface. On the top of this ballast was laid a stiff reinforced concrete base slab, around the perimeter of which was constructed a thick concrete wall acting as the main transference beam. Two internal cross-walls were provided as stiffening ribs; all walls being surmounted and tied together with a thin reinforced concrete top slab. Thus heavy, uneven and changing loads were spread over the bearing stratum and differential settlement was avoided by the transference of excess load from the weaker to the stronger zones in the ballast.

The Company has recently completed the construction, entirely in reinforced concrete, of a water tower of 240,000 gallons capacity and 80 ft in height for the Wainsford Urban District Council. A standard type of inverted raft was designed to spread the load over a ballast strata near the surface. The base of this raft was of some substance, being very heavily reinforced with its steel arranged radially. The concrete was vibrated, of exceptionally high quality, and well cured. Thus the design and construction was devised to obviate all types of cracking and settlement of the foundations.

A reinforced concrete retaining wall was required in the River Colne in connection with workshop extensions for the Watford Engineering Company. A cofferdam, consisting of two rows of steel sheetings, with ash in-filling, was built to enable excavation to be carried out down to the chalk stratum expected at a depth of 2 ft below the river bed. Where the chalk dipped and ballast of a variable nature appeared, hardcore was consolidated into this ballast, which was further restrained by driving concrete paving slabs into the base of the excavation. These slabs also acted as shuttering. The ballast and hardcore was then grouted and sealed with a 6 in. thick layer of concrete. This foundation acted as a base for the foot of the retaining wall which was keyed into it with U-shaped steel " dowel " reinforcement bars.

A retaining wall, 30 ft in height, at Willesden for Messrs W. W. Drinkwater Limited, created an entirely different problem. Contrary to expectation, subsoil investigations and direct loading tests indicated that, under certain conditions of weathering and saturation, the clay bearing stratum might not remain stable under full load. It was deemed advisable to support this wall on $17\frac{1}{2}''$ dia. West's Shell Piles and thus obtain a guaranteed structure. Numerous detailed analyses were carried out to obtain the best and most economical design, which was further complicated as this wall also acted as a boundary wall and it was necessary to restrict the projection of the footings beyond the face of the wall to a minimum. Finally, a counterfort wall was adopted, using $5\text{-}17\frac{1}{2}''$ dia. piles to support each counterfort. The three piles in the front and the one pile in the middle row were raked at 1 in 5, the rear pile being vertical. They were so designed and located as to withstand, in themselves, a large proportion of the combined pressures, loads and forces applying at the base of the wall. Thus full use was made of the high engineering qualities of West's Shell Piles.

West's Piling & Construction Company have a fully qualified Design Office, which is responsible to the Company for all project and contract designs. Its services are, entirely without obligation, at the disposal of prospective clients, consulting engineers or architects. The Company's engineers will be pleased to advise and assist in any capacity on problems connected with piling or reinforced concrete and allied construction. The Design Office staff is well-balanced, widely experienced and versatile, enabling any urgent work to be expedited when the occasion arises, to the benefit of clients and the Company's own Contracts Department. The Company welcomes the opportunity of discussing any project in its initial stages so that assistance can be given in developing the scheme and in producing a budget estimate for capital authorization. The Design Office can then complete a firm priced scheme design which, if accepted, can readily be used in the preparation of contract drawings. Finally, our contracts are carried out under expert and experienced supervision. It is by these thorough means that all work designed and constructed by the Company can be guaranteed.

West's Piling & Construction Company, although basically Piling and Foundation Specialists, are equipped to carry out any work of reinforced concrete construction. Contracts involving bulk excavation, road and drainage works and most civil engineering work connected with reinforced concrete structures have, in the past, been undertaken and completed with satisfaction both to our clients and to ourselves. The Company does not carry out sheet piling except as part of the main foundation contract or as a necessary part of the temporary works. Many successful sheet piling works have, however, been executed.

No contract is either too small or too large and all receive the same careful attention to the planning, quality, speedy execution and qualified supervision of the works.

REFERENCES

Civil Engineering Code of Practice No. 4. Foundations. Issued by the Institution of Civil Engineers.

Foundation Engineering, by Peck, Hanson & Thornburn. London, Chapman & Hall Ltd. (400 pages.)

The Design and Construction of Engineering Foundations, by F. D. C. Henry. London, E. & F. N. Spon Ltd. (550 pages.)

CHAPTER FOUR

RECENT CONTRACTS

A description of some of the contracts completed by West's Piling & Construction Company during recent years, together with notes on foundation problems which arose in connection with the contracts.

Stafford : A section of the piling after driving to set and installation of cores

Stafford : Part of the slab under construction

STAFFORD

GASHOLDER FOUNDATIONS

An order for a 2 million cubic feet capacity spirally-guided gasholder and steel tank was placed by the Corporation of Stafford before nationalization of the gas industry took place, and the design and construction of the foundation section, including sub-strata investigation, was carried out as a direct contract by West's Piling & Construction Company.

Owing to the unknown nature of the sub-soil it was decided to sink one 6 in. dia. borehole at the centre of the proposed gasholder site and also three around the periphery. These boreholes disclosed top soil for 5 to 6 ft, then a stratum of blue-brown clay and peat, about 11 ft thick, followed by a stratum of peat down to 40 ft depth, which overlay a stratum of running sand, 4 to 8 ft thick. Finally gravel was found at an average depth of 45 ft.

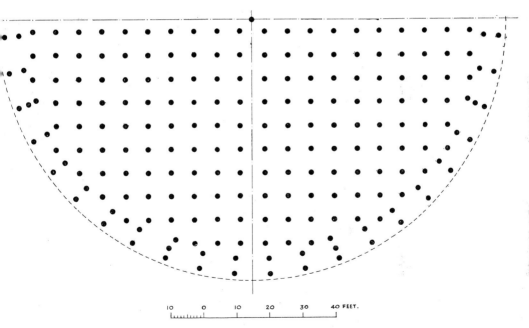

Stafford : Half-plan illustrating layout of piles. Loading : 50 tons per pile

It was therefore decided to adopt a scheme incorporating 431-17½″ dia. West's Shell Piles to take a maximum individual load of 50 tons.

Driving was carried out by means of a large-type mobile piling outfit, constructed from a 1½ cubic yd capacity excavator, powered by a 116-h.p. diesel engine, and a 65 ft steam-driven piling frame. Pile lengths varied from 47 ft 6 in. to 70 ft, and all the piling was carried out between August and November, 1949.

Each pile was driven to a resistance to penetration, calculated from the Hiley Formula, using a safety factor of 3 and utilizing a 3-ton hammer, dropping 30 in. For the majority of the piling a set of 14 blows to the last inch of penetration was obtained for piles 50 to 55 ft long and a set of 17 blows to the last inch for piles 55 to 57 ft long, but for the few piles longer than these ranges, sets of over 20 blows per inch were obtained. The upper photo on page 38 shows a section of the piling after the piles had been driven to the required set and completed with reinforced concrete cores.

The 8,000 pile shells—17½ in. dia. × 3 ft. long—which were required for this contract were cast on site adjacent to the location of the holder.

Supported on the piles, and at ground level, a reinforced concrete slab was constructed, 155 ft dia. and 10 in. thick. The concrete was a normal mix of 1 part cement, 2 parts sand and 4 parts aggregate and the specification called for a minimum crushing strength of 3,000 lb. per sq. inch, at 28 days, which was easily exceeded. The lower photo on page 38 shows this slab being constructed on a 3 in. mat of lean mass concrete to protect the soffit.

Stafford : The completed foundation slab

40

SALFORD

FOUNDATIONS FOR VERTICAL RETORTS

A large section of this site was composed of filled-in material overlying a soft clay stratum which gradually became firmer in depth and it was decided to use piles. In order to provide suitable support for the loading under consideration 151-14½″ dia. and 288-17½″ dia. West's reinforced concrete shell piles were incorporated in the design so as to accommodate 40-ton and 60-ton vertical loading. The layout of piles and the loading at various points is shown below.

Driving was carried out with a West's mobile 14RB excavator pile frame and driving operations disclosed a sub-stratum which gave the correct set at an average depth of 20 ft to 25 ft.

A particular feature of the Salford installation necessitated the retort house floor being elevated approximately 10 ft. As the piles were capped

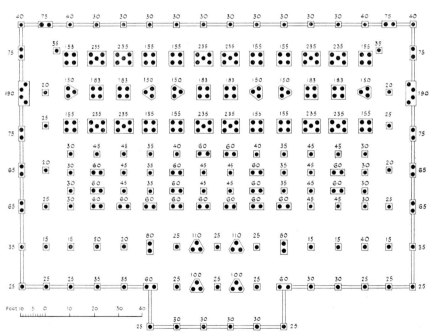

FIGURES INDICATE PILECAP LOADING (IN TONS)

Salford : Pile layout and loading plan

41

at ground level it was necessary to transfer the retort house loading to the piled foundations through reinforced concrete supporting columns which are shown below with the existing plant in the background. The lower photograph shows the reinforced concrete retort house floor slab nearing completion and preparatory to receiving the retort bench steelwork.

SALFORD

Right : Construction of supporting columns for retort house floor slab

Below : Retort house floor slab nearing completion

BOURNE END

FOUNDATIONS FOR PULPING MACHINE SHOP

This interesting civil engineering project was carried out on the works of Messrs Jackson's Millboard & Fibre Company Ltd at Bourne End in the Thames Valley between Maidenhead and Marlow. A considerable amount of site clearance had to be carried out for which a 19RB Ruston Excavator was used with $\frac{5}{8}$ cubic yard dragline equipment. Two large lagoons which had been used for settling the effluent from the works had to be emptied, and the sludge excavated and carted away—some 10,000 cubic yards in all being removed. Two of the remaining lagoons are shown in the background of the photograph below, which also shows concreting of the floor slabs in progress and the commencement of the erection of the steelwork.

All the steel stanchions and heavy machinery on the ground floor were carried on mass concrete foundations taken down to the stratum of Thames Ballast which necessitated excavation to various depths, from 7 ft to 20 ft. Several hundred foundation bolts were incorporated in this section for securing the stanchion bases.

Bourne End :
Concreting of floor
slabs in progress

Bourne End :
First floor
constructed of
reinforced concrete
and concrete
encased R.S.J's

The reinforced concrete ground floors, utilizing a mix of four parts $\frac{3}{4}$ in. to $\frac{3}{16}$ in. aggregate and two parts of sharp sand to one part of normal setting Portland cement, were all laid to falls to facilitate drainage, and were constructed in different thicknesses to suit the varying loads which were, in turn, transmitted to reinforced concrete beams spanning between the mass concrete bases. At a height of 22 ft above the ground floor, the first floor was constructed of reinforced concrete and rolled-steel joists encased in concrete as shown above, and had an area of 1,600 sq. yds.

Outside the main building a reinforced concrete storage area of 7,000 sq. yds, complete with crane gantry, was constructed to facilitate the handling and storage of raw materials and the loading of finished products. Along the river frontage a reinforced concrete retaining wall was erected 165 ft long—8 ft 6 in. high. The photograph below shows the storage area with crane gantry in use, behind which is the completed main building.

Owing to the shortage of local labour and in order to maintain a satisfactory labour strength it was found necessary to erect a camp for the workmen consisting of two concrete and timber buildings for living and sleeping accommodation, while for meals West's Piling personnel were allowed the facilities of Messrs Jackson's excellent canteen.

Bourne End :
Storage area with
crane gantry in
front of main
building

44

FAWLEY

NEW REFINERY FOR
ESSO PETROLEUM COMPANY

West's Piling & Construction Company made a large contribution towards the construction of this new refinery, one of the largest in full operation outside the U.S.A. The four main contracts entrusted to the Company consisted of piled foundations for the following :

1. Pipe Trestles and Pump House. This included a complicated system of transverse raking piles for 57 bents of the approach trestles carrying numerous pipe-lines to and from the jetty, and piled supports for the 48-in. diameter main effluent water line. A total of 986 piles, consisting of 690-20″ diameter vertical and 185-17½″ diameter rakers, were driven in this contract.

2. Ballast Water Tank. This 100-ft diameter tank, weighing some 11,200 tons when loaded, was supported on 185-20″ diameter vertical piles.

3. Oil Storage Tanks. These tanks, of up to 150 ft in diameter, incorporated a total of 664-20″ and 284-17½″ diameter vertical piles.

4. Cooler Box. This intricate foundation contract was carried out in difficult conditions as it was situated in almost the only " square yard " of space available in the refinery area.

All vertical piles were driven through a soft layer of clay and are resting on a thick gravel stratum overlying the stiff Barton Clay, an Eocene formation which is the youngest Kianozoic or Tertiary representative, presumed to be some 30 million years old.

An interesting feature was that raker piles for the trestles were essential to withstand uplift forces up to 35 tons. Tests proved that the soft clay and river gravel strata did not provide sufficient frictional resistance to fulfil this requirement. It was thus necessary to drive the raker piles through the soft clay and river gravel strata into the stiff and sticky Barton Clay. This entailed very prolonged hard driving. Further tests proved that when the raker piles penetrated into the Barton Clay, it provided the necessary adhesion to prevent the piles from moving when a 35-ton uplift force was applied to them.

The extreme mobility of West's piling equipment, which included

Fawley : The specially adapted raking frames

Fawley : Progress of piling and slab construction

specially adapted raking frames, permitted these important projects to be kept to schedule.

Sulphate resisting cement was first introduced by West's to the Clients for the foundation concrete.

The new refinery covers an area of 970 acres, and has a modern cracking plant with numerous by-product plants ; it has a capacity to handle 46,000 barrels of crude oil per day, a storage capacity of 5,600,000 barrels of oil and a yearly production of 5,000,000 tons of petrol (equivalent to the yearly average consumption of 2,000,000 motor-cars). Finally, its jetty can berth simultaneously four 39,000-ton specially built modern tankers.

A general view of the Crude Units of the Refinery

An Esso photo by William Martin, Southampton

Thames Haven : Driving in progress. Two tracked piling machines installing 20" dia. piles

Thames Haven : Completed piling on two tanks, slab construction in background, test pile cap under construction in foreground

48

THAMES HAVEN

PILING FOR OIL STORAGE TANKS

The London and Thames Haven Oil Wharves Ltd storage depot is situated on the North bank of the River Thames between the Shell Haven and Coryton Refineries and near to the village of Stanford-le-Hope in Essex.

Many tanks have been constructed previously on this site but they are built on reinforced concrete raft foundations and owing to the poor bearing capacity of the sub-soil tilting of several tanks has occurred.

For the present project the four tanks are to be larger and taller than the previous ones, resulting in heavier ground loads and the Consulting Engineers, Messrs L. G. Mouchel & Partners, Ltd, decided that piled foundations should be incorporated.

Our contract consisted of 20″ diameter West's Shell Piles approximately 50 ft long with a bearing capacity of 98 tons each. Whilst installing the piles it was found that they penetrated to a depth of 45 ft through alluvial deposits almost under their own weight but from this depth onwards the hammer had to be used for the heavy driving necessary to overcome the resistance to penetration of the ballast stratum in which the piles were founded.

The design incorporated fairly close spacing of the piles and during driving operations a certain amount of uplift was produced, as is not uncommon in these circumstances. All the tanks will be subjected to a water test before being put into use, however, and as oil is lighter than water all the uplift should be overcome before actual operational conditions obtain. Whilst in use the foundations will be subjected to a considerable variation of loading as the tanks will be filled and emptied frequently.

The contract which commenced in adverse winter weather was completed well on schedule to suit the requirements of Messrs John Laing & Son Ltd, who are constructing the concrete slabs, and the London and Thames Haven Oil Wharves Ltd, who are controlling the erection of the steel tanks.

Isle of Grain : Piled foundations for intermediate storage tanks

Isle of Grain : Foundation slab (*Photos by courtesy of British Petroleum Co. Ltd*)

ISLE OF GRAIN

PILING FOR REFINERY UNITS

The Isle of Grain lies directly across the Thames Estuary from the holiday resort of Southend, and the site of the Kent Oil Refinery of the British Petroleum Company covers an area of nearly 2,000 acres on this promontory formed by the confluence of the rivers Thames and Medway on the north coast of the county of Kent.

Below the top soil is a stratum of alluvial silt with poor bearing qualities which overlies a gravel stratum occurring at different depths over the site with a maximum thickness of about 15 ft but thinning out to negligible thickness in certain locations. Beneath the gravel lies London clay to a great depth.

Work on the construction of the refinery commenced in 1950 and the first cargo of crude oil arrived in October, 1952. Our present contract is for piling in the Expansion Project where over 10,000 piles are envisaged varying from 20 ft to 70 ft in length, to support refinery units and storage tanks. Pile driving commenced in April 1956, and the main units are scheduled for completion by the end of 1957.

Extensions are planned which will increase the number of jetties to nine, in order to accommodate the new oil tankers up to 32,000 tons recently constructed for the British Tanker Company.

The cost of the complete refinery will be about £70 millions, and when the Expansion Project is in operation there will be capacity to process 7·1 million tons of crude oil per annum, making it one of the largest refineries in Europe. The principal products obtained will be motor spirit, kerosene, tractor vaporizing oil, gas oil, fuel oils and lubricants.

Sir Robert McAlpine & Sons, Ltd, are the main civil contractors; Rendel, Palmer & Tritton are the consulting engineers for the civil engineering work in the project, and George Wimpey & Co. Ltd, have been appointed main mechanical contractors.

51

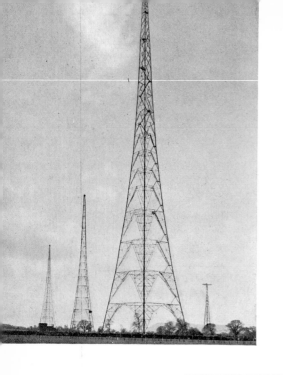

Criggion :
The completed towers

Criggion :
A completed footing ready to receive the structure

Criggion :
The various types of machine used for piling, including a raker outfit

52

CRIGGION

PILED FOUNDATIONS FOR RADIO TOWERS

In 1942 the Ministry of Works approved a scheme for the erection of a new Radio Station for the G.P.O at Criggion, which lies between Welshpool and Oswestry, in Montgomeryshire. The upper photograph (opposite) shows the masts as they appeared on April 7, 1943. The steelwork in each tower weighed over 200 tons and the height is 600 ft.

The foundations for the masts were on 263 West's Shell Piles, which varied in depth from 25 ft to 94 ft. To carry the resultant thrust at the base of the columns eight raker piles were driven at each corner, making 96 of this type of pile for the three towers, and the completed footing ready to receive the structure is clearly seen on the centre photograph.

The various types of machines—including that for driving the raker piles—are shown on the lower photograph.

The structure was the first of hundreds of towers of a similar type for which West's Piling & Construction Company have provided piled foundations during the past eight years.

Gurnard Pines : The swimming pool

GURNARD PINES, I.O.W.

SWIMMING POOL FOR HOLIDAY CAMP

West's Piling & Construction Company have also been concerned with the design and construction of bathing pools in reinforced concrete, of which Gurnard Pines is one example.

Situated on a hill overlooking Cowes in the Isle of Wight and the Solent, and surrounded by wooded countryside, the Gurnard Pines Holiday Camp possesses the swimming pool illustrated which was constructed by West's Piling in the camp grounds to provide bathing facilities on the spot.

The reinforced concrete bathing pool is 100 ft long by 30 ft wide, varying from 3 ft water depth at the shallow end to 7 ft near the diving board, the water level being about 2 ft below the top of the bath. Internally it is finished in colour and surrounding the top of the pool is a multi-coloured pressed paving slab walkway and a concrete foot-channel.

At the shallow end is a fountain-type aerator from which water runs down a flight of steps giving access to the bath while at the deep end a reinforced concrete diving stand is erected, with stages at different heights.

The filter house is built in the banking near the deep end, the roof being at a level of 2 ft above the walkway around the bath and formed of hardened asphalt to permit its use for sunbathing.

The filter plant is capable of purifying the whole of the water in the bath once every eight hours and is provided with a gas type chlorinator. In addition a gas type ammoniator is fitted to work in conjunction with the chlorinator to form chloramine process. Heating is supplied by a coke fired boiler capable of imparting 500,000 B.Th.U.'s per hour to the water.

55

Stepney : Piling completed for one block and excavation for beams in progress

Photo by S. W. Newbury, courtesy of W. Curtis Green, R.A., Son and Lloyd

Stepney : A completed block constructed by the main contractor

56

STEPNEY

FOUNDATIONS FOR SEVEN BLOCKS OF FLATS

In view of the increasing importance of the topical subject of the construction of houses and flats we are pleased to be able to publish a few details of the type of piled foundation contracts for housing schemes which we have constructed for the London County Council and other authorities.

One example of this type of contract was for the Berner Estate, Christian Street, Stepney, E.1, a development plan which consisted of seven blocks of flats and included reinforced concrete ground beams supported on 589 $17\frac{1}{2}''$ diameter West's Shell Piles.

The piles were driven by two mobile piling machines through filling consisting of brick rubble, foundations of old cottage property and building basements, into a ballast stratum which gave suitable resistance to penetration at depths from 12 to 15 ft below ground level.

The nature of the stratum of filled material resulted in an appreciable amount of obstruction to piling operations and the excavation for these obstructions entailed the removal of several thousand cubic yards of concrete, brickwork and drains.

The upper photograph (opposite) was taken when piling was nearing completion. The pile core reinforcement can clearly be seen projecting into the trench which has been excavated preparatory to receiving the reinforced concrete ground beams for one block. The lower photograph shows one of the completed blocks.

Housing Construction on West's Shell Piles in the London Area

CLEVE HALL ESTATE,
Camberwell, S.E.5

Foundations for five blocks of flats were constructed on this site, incorporating 230 West's Shell Piles, 17½″ dia., with caps and beams. The photograph above shows piling, and excavation for beams, while on the right is shown construction in progress by the Building Department of the Camberwell Borough Council under the direction of the Borough Engineer and Surveyor, John Clapp, A.M.Inst.C.E., M.Inst.Mun.E. (Client: The Camberwell Borough Council. Architects: Howes and Jackman.)

FLAMSTEED ESTATE,
Greenwich, S.E.10
(left)

This contract consisted of piling, caps and beams to six blocks of flats in all, involving a total of 305 West's Shell Piles, 14½″ dia.
The general view of the site shows several blocks under construction by the main contractor, Stewart and Partners Ltd. (Client: The London County Council. Architects: Howes and Jackman.)

58

Reproduced by courtesy of the London County Council

HOUNSLOW (right)

The foundation slab nearing completion for a new block of flats at Wellington Road South, incorporating 102 West's Shell Piles, $14\frac{1}{2}''$ dia.

This site was located on the boundary of an old gravel pit, which resulted in the piles being relatively deep over the area of the pit and short where the undisturbed Thames ballast stratum was encountered at a depth of approximately 7 ft. (Client: The Heston and Isleworth Borough Council. Borough Engineer and Surveyor: O. P. F. Hilton, A.M.Inst.C.E.)

PATMORE STREET, Battersea, S.W.8 (left)

The photograph depicts construction by the main contractor proceeding on a block of flats founded on 79 piles, $14\frac{1}{2}''$ dia. It was necessary to drive the piles through brick rubble to a set in the underlying ballast stratum, an operation for which West's Shell Piles proved particularly suited. (Client: The London County Council. Architects: DeMetz and Birks, F/F.R.I.B.A.)

Reproduced by courtesy of the London County Council

BANDON ROAD, Bethnal Green, E.2 (right)

Large block of flats nearing completion by the main contractors, Lavendar McMillan Ltd, on the site of the L.C.C. Housing Scheme. This foundation incorporated 352 West's Shell Piles, $14\frac{1}{2}''$ dia. In the clay sub-strata on this site in the Thames Estuary, frequent lenses of Thames ballast occurred, some of which were shallow enough to be removed. Others, however, were of sufficient depth and thickness to provide adequate resistance for load-bearing and were utilized in this way. (Client: The London County Council. Architects: DeMetz and Birks, F/F.R.I.B.A.)

59

Reproduced by courtesy of the London County Council

Bankside : Completed building

Bankside : Two mobile piling machines in action

BANKSIDE, SOUTHWARK

PILING FOR HEADQUARTERS BUILDING

CENTRAL ELECTRICITY AUTHORITY

The piling for the foundations for the new National Headquarters of the Central Electricity Authority was carried out by West's Piling & Construction Company on a bomb-damaged site at the south side of the River Thames at Southwark, London, S.E.1, adjacent to the Bankside Power Station.

The total number of piles installed was 648 and all were standard $17\frac{1}{2}''$ dia. West's Shell Piles with lengths varying from 11 to 35 ft, each being capable of supporting a 60-ton load.

The lower photograph (opposite) shows piling in progress with two tracked diesel machines, together with earth-moving and reinforced concrete work being carried out simultaneously by other contractors in view of the urgency of the project. It may be noted that the piling area was excavated down to the required final level of 12 ft below normal ground level.

From this excavated level the sub-strata consists of about 10 ft of fairly soft sand and silt with some pebbles overlying an 11-ft stratum of firm sand and gravel, below which there is typical London blue clay. Although at the time of tendering it was not known if this gravel stratum could readily be penetrated, the specification called for all piles to be driven at least 5 ft into the London clay—or to such other depth as might be required by the engineer after the results of driving the first piles were ascertained.

One pile, 19 ft long, which obtained a suitable set in the gravel stratum was tested with a load of 150 tons and gave very satisfactory results. It was therefore decided to accept piles which met with the requisite resistance to penetration in the gravel stratum without insisting on entering the London clay and the majority of the piles were therefore between 10 and 20 ft long.

Llanelly : Switching station

Rye House : Switching station

OTHER CONTRACTS FOR THE
CENTRAL ELECTRICITY AUTHORITY

LLANELLY

SWITCHING STATION AND TERMINAL TOWER—TROSTRE WORKS

The photograph opposite shows the nearly complete switching station, supported on 130 West's Shell Piles and the terminal tower (on the left) founded on eight piles. In both cases $17\frac{1}{2}''$ dia. piles were driven through deep fill over virgin marshy ground. The main contractors were Messrs Hinkin & Frewin, of Oxford, and Messrs B.I.C. Construction Co. Ltd (tower).

PENRITH

Owing to the peaty nature of the ground in this area of the Penrith 132-kV transmission line, it was necessary to install piled foundations for towers Nos. 307 and 308. This involved a total of 24 West's Shell Piles, $17\frac{1}{2}''$ dia., driven to depths of 25 to 35 ft. The piles were relatively lightly loaded ; a factor influencing their number in this case being the frictional resistance to uplift, here approximately 10 tons per pile. Pile shells in contact with the peat stratum were manufactured of " Ciment Fondu " to resist the deleterious nature of the sub-soil.

SWANSEA

TIR JOHN GENERATING STATION

Piling was carried out for the foundations to the coal handling plant structure at Tir John Generating Station for the South Wales Division of the C.E.A. This contract involved a total of 16 West's Shell Piles, $14\frac{1}{2}''$ dia.

RYE HOUSE, Nr. Hoddesdon, Herts.

SWITCHING STATION ADJOINING RYE HOUSE POWER STATION

These foundations involved the installation of 122 West's Shell Piles, $17\frac{1}{2}''$ dia., driven to an average depth of 40 to 45 ft. A further 44 piles were subsequently driven for foundations to the transmission line for Messrs W. T. Henley's Telegraph Works Co. Ltd.

PORTISHEAD, Nr. Bristol

The illustration overleaf depicts piling in progress on the site of the administration block for the Portishead " B " Power Station. This contract consisted of 244 West's Shell Piles, $17\frac{1}{2}''$ dia., driven to an average depth of

Portishead : Piling in progress

Poole : Piling concreted to correct level, with 120-ton test load on a pile on Tank No. 2   (Photo by courtesy of C.E.A.)

30 to 35 ft. In the background, Portishead " A " Power Station may be seen.

KEADBY-SCUNTHORPE TRANSMISSION LINE

The 198-ft high river crossing towers on both the Keadby and Gunness sides of the River Trent are each supported on eight West's Shell Piles, $17\frac{1}{2}''$ dia. This was necessitated by silt deposits extending to a depth of 45 to 50 ft in the area of the transmission line crossing.

POOLE POWER STATION
PILING FOR OIL TANKS AND ANCILLARY PLANT

Poole Harbour, Dorset, has an excellent approach from the sea and is well protected from heavy water. Having a boundary at high water of approximately 100 miles, it is a popular venue for yachts and smaller sailing craft, while in its centre is Brownsea Island, beautifully wooded with firs and pines. It is thought that the first radio message transmitted across the sea was sent by Marconi from here to the mainland.

Additional work has been carried out for the Central Electricity Authority adjacent to the existing Power Station, but before piling commenced the land had to be reclaimed and many thousands of tons of filling were imported by Messrs George Wimpey & Co. Ltd, who were entrusted with this section of the work.

Two oil tanks have been installed leaving space for a further tank and adjacent work includes bund and retaining walls, the primary object of these latter being to localize fire should it break out, as it is appreciated that the huge expanse of water in Poole Harbour would be seriously menaced should this occur. Other work included a pump-house and numerous trestles for supporting pipes and culverts for conveying water.

Borings indicated that there was a stratum of " Potters Clay " about 40 ft thick overlying a thick stratum of Kimmeridge clay, both of which have a high shear value and little water content.

Various experiments were carried out with different lengths of piles including test loading but it was decided to leave the piles on a high set repeated twelve times when driven into the Potters clay rather than continue with excessive driving in order to penetrate the Kimmeridge clay. As the working load of the piles was 40 tons and a safety factor of 3 was demanded by the C.E.A., it was necessary to provide kentledge of 120 tons as shown in the photograph and all loading tests were considered satisfactory.

250 piles were driven for each tank at 5 ft 6 in. centres, and during driving operations the ground lifted 18 in. in the centre while the average lift of each pile during driving was from $\frac{1}{2}$ in. to $\frac{5}{8}$ in. In the retaining wall section 177 piles were driven to a rake of 1 in 3, and over the whole contract the pile lengths vary from 37 ft to 84 ft.

Poole : Circular shuttering being fixed to top of piles
(Photo by courtesy of the Central Electricity Authority)

Tilbury : Switching Station, showing part of 275-kV Tilbury/Elstree line

Alterations to the design of the tanks necessitated the raising of the pile core level to approximately 2 ft above the ground level and when the pile shells did not project sufficiently this work was carried out by means of circular steel shuttering and in-situ concrete.

The contract for the construction of the retaining walls, culverts and tank slabs was carried out by Messrs George Wimpey & Co. Ltd, to the design of the C.E.A. (Southern Division).

TILBURY
Piling for 132-kV Switching Station

The above contract consisted of driving 450 West's Shell Piles 17½″ dia. to an average depth of 45 to 50 ft, the safe working load on each pile being 35 tons.

The original date of commencement was to have been January or early February 1953, but considerable delay was experienced owing to the disastrous floods which occurred on the week-end of January 31st/February 1st causing widespread damage and tragic loss of life over such a large section of the eastern coastline.

The two piling machines scheduled to commence the contract were actually being transferred when news was received that the site was inundated by the sea and movements were hastily stopped.

A start was finally made on March 2nd and, in an endeavour to compensate for lost time, a third piling machine was put in use, later joined by a fourth.

Progress was very satisfactory and piling was concluded by April 20th, very little after the original completion date as tendered.

An examination of the driving record of a typical pile (No. 162) and adjacent borehole, reveals the following information about the sub-strata in this locality. The surface consisted of ash fill 6 in. to 1 ft in thickness, providing an excellent working area for the piling machines. Under the ash was a thin layer of top soil overlying a 2 ft 6 in. thick stratum of hard clay. This gave way to soft grey clay and peat down to a depth of about 40 ft. Driving resistance to about half this depth was recorded as negligible.

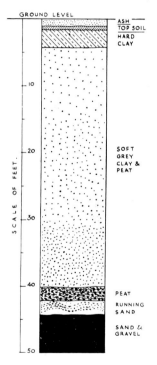

Tilbury :

Diagram showing

strata

BELVEDERE

Above: Four machines at work on the main station site

Right: Piling on an oil tank site. Here piles have been built up to 5 ft above ground level in accordance with design requirements

68

A 2 ft thickness of peat and 2 ft of running sand were then encountered before the load bearing stratum of sand and gravel was reached.

Pile No. 162 reached a final " set " of 12 blows to 1 in. penetration into the sand and gravel stratum at a depth of 45 ft, and was driven by a 3-ton hammer with a free drop of 30 in. The pre-calculated theoretical " set " according to the Hiley Formula was 6 blows per inch of penetration.

A test load of 52 tons, i.e. the working load of 35 tons plus 50 per cent. overload, was subsequently applied to pile No. 162, and the final settlement, after removal of the load, was 0·07 in., which was considered highly satis-factory. The test took place over a period of 7 days.

Owing to the presence of sulphates in the ground, sulphate-resisting cement was used for the pile cores. Standard Portland cement shells were used, however, as it was considered that sulphates would have no deleterious effects on the well matured stock selected for use.

In conclusion, it may be noted that one after-effect of the flooding which affected the contract was a serious shortage of lodging accommodation in the Tilbury area. This was overcome by the erection on the site of two dormitory huts, equipped with suitable amenities for the men. The use of the C.E.A. canteen, catering for the men constructing the adjacent generating station, was appreciated by West's Piling employees.

BELVEDERE

Piling for Generating Station

The site of the Belvedere Generating Station lies on Erith Marsh on the south side of the Thames Estuary, opposite the great Ford Works at Dagen-ham. The scheme for the construction of the station reached the practical stage of test borings two to three years prior to the commencement of general site preparations. From these it was clear that a large number of piles would be required to support the main station building, chimneys and ancillary buildings, and resulting from direct negotiations with the Central Electricity Authority, West's piling system was selected for the project.

The test borings revealed that the site consisted of undulating layers of top soil, clay, peat and alluvial silt to a depth of approximately 36 ft below original ground level, before any bearing stratum was met. At this depth lay a bed of sandy ballast varying from 8 ft to 30 ft in thickness, and below this was blue clay overlying deep ballast beds, the latter being met at approxi-mately 55 ft to 60 ft below ground level. It was intended that the piling should penetrate into the ballast stratum to a depth of 2 to 3 ft and that the piles would, therefore, be approximately 33 ft long. In certain areas where the ballast stratum thinned out to 8 ft to 9 ft, it was anticipated that the piles might well pass through the ballast without reaching a satisfactory set. This, in fact, occurred in the north-west corner of the building where the piles penetrated 50 to 55 ft.

BELVEDERE

Left : Driving raker piles on the chimney foundation

USKMOUTH-MELKSHAM

Right : Typical towers supported on West's Shell Piles

In July 1955 test piling commenced, and in the following month, after the main contractor had reduced the general site level, the piling to the northern section of the station commenced. In the following winter and spring approximately 4,300 piles were driven, using 37RB, 33RB and 24RB outfits. Of these piles 2,600 were 20″ dia., designed to carry 110 tons and 84 tons, and 1,700 were $17\frac{1}{2}″$ dia., designed to carry 68 tons and 55 tons, according to the reinforcement used.

In the course of the work the Central Electricity Authority decided that the station should become partially oil-burning, as a result of which a tank farm was designed and three tanks were piled, using 468 piles of 20″ dia.

Throughout the work, test loads were applied to selected piles and the results indicated that the bearing strata would satisfactorily carry the designed load.

The northern section of the station piling was completed in scheduled time and a further contract of approximately 3,000-20″ piles has now started on the southern section.

USKMOUTH-MELKSHAM

275-kV TRANSMISSION LINE

Uskmouth Power Station, near Newport, is one of the main Central Electricity Authority stations built since the war, and Melksham sub-station is a large switching and transforming station from which lines radiate to the Midlands, South-East, Southern and South-West England. The Uskmouth/Melksham transmission line forms the main link between these two important terminal points.

The length of the route is about 14 miles in Monmouthshire from Uskmouth to Beachley, then $2\frac{1}{2}$ miles in three spans of the Severn Crossing from Beachley to Aust, followed by about $28\frac{1}{2}$ miles from Aust (Glos.) to Melksham (Wilts.), making a total of 45 miles.

On the two land sections of the line standard designs of transmission line towers are used, each 120 ft high and weighing 8 tons (average). For the Severn Crossing, however, four specially designed towers will be used, the two anchor towers being 100 ft and 175 ft high, and the two intermediate crossing towers 480 ft high. The total weight of steel in these four towers will be 470 tons.

On the Uskmouth/Beachley section 10 miles of the route crosses very bad marshland, and $17\frac{1}{2}″$ dia. West's Shell Piles have been used here for the foundations of 47 towers out of a total of 60. In addition 4 towers have also been piled at the run-in for the 132-kV line. The numbers of piles at the towers vary from 8 to 20 and the lengths of the piles vary from 23 ft to 73 ft.

For the Severn Crossing towers specially designed concrete foundations will be used and on the remainder of the line concrete foundations of a standard type are being designed and installed by J. L. Eve Construction Co. Ltd, the main contractors for this project.

71

Rochdale :

Piling on site. Normal section completed and special section in progress within periphery of old holder.

Rochdale :

Mandrel points used for piercing the existing concrete tank bottom.

Rochdale :

The holder erected by Messrs R. & J. Dempster Ltd.

ROCHDALE

FOUNDATIONS FOR GASHOLDER

During 1947 the piling for the foundations for a new 2 million cu. ft capacity spirally guided gasholder was driven at the Rochdale Gasworks.

The periphery of the new gasholder overlapped the site of an old holder which had been of similar capacity and which it now replaces. A drawing dated 1870 of the old holder tank showed a clay puddle bottom approximately 2 ft thick on which a covering of sandstone slabs 3 in. thick was shown to keep the puddle true and in good condition. It was anticipated that there would be no difficulty in driving piles through the 3 in. slabs to a normal set, but the first attempts to drive such piles were not successful. It was therefore decided to excavate the filling down to the bottom of the tank at one place to examine the slabs, when it was found that the bottom of the tank consisted of solid lime-bonded concrete with old brick aggregate, with an average 18 in. thickness.

Blasting and boring were considered, but eventually mandrel driving was carried out with the standard point as shown at A in the centre photograph. Three $11\frac{1}{2}$ in. dia. 3 ft long mandrels are in the background for comparison. It was found possible to pierce the concrete tank bottom, although not sufficiently to allow normal pile driving. A special mandrel point was then designed 18 in. dia. tapering to $11\frac{1}{2}$ in. dia. and fitted with a standard mandrel spigot as shown at B. Driving this head through the concrete slab resulted in holes over 18 in. dia. and it was then possible to follow with standard tubular concrete piles.

Outside the periphery of the old holder tank there was a considerable variation in the pile lengths due to the undulating nature of the rock base. Test boring was carried out and confirmed that the short piles were in fact based on solid rock and not on boulders although pile lengths varied between 19 ft and 44 ft. The use of West's Shell Piling, therefore, was particularly advantageous. The sub-strata investigation showed that the holder area was most probably on the site of the old course of the River Roche, which would account for the variation in rock level.

The total piling involved 357-$17\frac{1}{2}''$ piles with an aggregate length of over 10,000 ft. The piles penetrated through the soft strata of clay and silt until arrested by the hard rock stratum. The site was waterlogged to about 3 ft below ground level, and careful attention was necessary to ensure dry piles.

The holder, erected by Messrs R. & J. Dempster Ltd, has a capacity of $1\frac{1}{2}$ million cu. ft at present, but there is provision for an extra lift to increase this to 2 million cu. ft. The weight of steelwork in the holder is 460 tons and the volume of water in the tank is $3\frac{1}{2}$ million gallons weighing approximately 15,000 tons.

Llanelly : West's mobile piling machines operating in the warehouse area

Trostre Works : General view

LLANELLY

TROSTRE TINPLATE WORKS

The new steelworks plant erected at Llanelly for the Steel Company of Wales Ltd comprises a pickling department, five-stand tandem mill, cleaning lines, annealing department, temper mills, shearing department and warehouse, to handle coils of strip produced at Abbey Works, Margam.

The piling contract carried out by West's Piling & Construction Company involved a total of over 27,000 piles for the whole site, the rate of driving being from 1,000 to 1,500 piles per month.

The site of the works is approximately $1\frac{1}{2}$ miles long by $\frac{3}{4}$ mile wide consisting of undulating ground, for which West's mobile pile-drivers are admirably suited, and the warehouse area, 720 ft by 140 ft, is elevated approximately 12 ft. The sub-strata vary considerably over the site and pile lengths ranged from 7 ft 6 in. to over 50 ft.

The upper photograph (opposite) shows our pile-drivers almost completing the piling for the warehouse area, which is ready to receive the reinforced concrete floor. Although the warehouse department was the last building to be required in the plant itself, its progress was speeded up to enable it to be used as a temporary store and general purpose building during the constructional period.

The main contractors for this project were Messrs Robert M. Douglas (Contractors) Ltd, of Birmingham, and the consultants were L. G. Mouchel & Partners Ltd, of London, S.W.1.

St. Albans : Piling with mobile outfit alongside existing gas plant

Below : Completed retort house

Right :

Diagram
showing
sub-strata

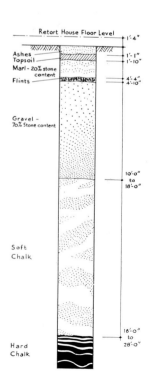

76

ST. ALBANS

FOUNDATIONS FOR VERTICAL RETORTS

The vertical retort plant extension at St. Albans Gasworks is constructed on piles disposed as shown on the plan below, on which, also, are indicated the loads which have to be carried.

The sub-strata upon which the vertical retort house is erected are shown on the diagram on the left and it should be particularly noticed that, though there is an excellent bearing stratum at the 10 ft to 18 ft level, it was considered desirable to penetrate this zone and carry the piles to the hard chalk stratum which quickly slopes between 18 ft to 28 ft over the site.

The installation of 40 50-inch retorts, built since the war, started gas-making in January 1948.

Below : Pile layout and loading plan

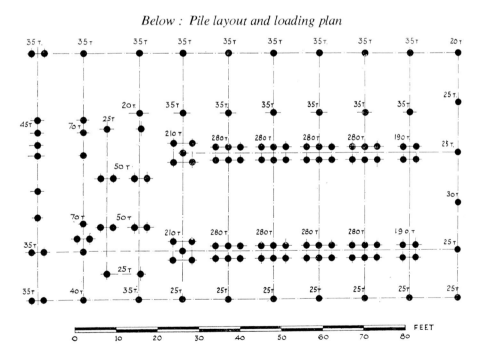

Southampton :

Ocean Terminal from the air —the Queen Mary *is alongside the opposite berth*

Southampton :

A mobile piling machine in action on the Ocean Dock site

CONTRACTS AT
SOUTHAMPTON DOCKS

Numerous and extensive contracts have been, and are being, carried out by West's Piling & Construction Company at Southampton Docks, involving diverse engineering problems and varied types of construction. West's Shell Piles are particularly suitable for work here, due to the exceptional variations in the broken sub-strata which are a feature of the dock area. The experience gained in overcoming these problems has enabled us to be of particular service to a variety of clients.

The typical contracts illustrated here may be of particular interest. In addition, work has been carried out for Rowntree & Company Limited ; British Transport Commission ; J. Rank Limited ; Parsons Engineering Company Limited ; Firestone Tyre & Rubber Company Limited ; W. & R. Jacob & Company Limited ; W. E. Chivers & Sons Limited.

PASSENGER TERMINAL, OCEAN DOCK

The foundations of the new Passenger Terminal for British Railways at the Ocean Dock, Southampton, are built on West's Shell Piles of two standard sizes which, being driven to a " resistance to penetration " calculated from the Hiley Formula, varied in length from 30 ft to 75 ft.

A 65-ft steam-driven piling outfit, utilizing a 5-ton steam hammer drove 195-20″ dia. piles with a bearing capacity of 90 tons each, and the mobile diesel-driven piling outfit shown opposite, utilizing a 3-ton drop hammer, drove 433-17½″ dia. piles with a bearing capacity of 60 tons each.

Reinforced concrete caps were built on the piles to carry the superstructure, the steelwork of which, amounting to some 2,300 tons, was erected by Cargo Fleet Iron Co. Ltd, of London, and the general building was carried out by Staverton Builders Ltd, of Totnes, Devon.

Cargo and stores are handled on the ground floor of the building while at the first floor level passengers embark and disembark by means of three twin turret telescopic enclosed gangways, constructed in aluminium alloy and operating from an external platform.

Numerous facilities are available to passengers awaiting customs examination of their luggage, including cable and telegraph offices, buffets and information bureaux. Passengers afterwards proceed to the ground floor by any of the 20 lifts and 4 escalators whilst luggage is handled

Left : Berth 102. Piling in progress on the dock-side

Below : Berth 102. Completed building. Exterior quayside view from east end

by 4 conveyors, the entrances to all of which being closed when necessary by steel rolling shutters.

A special sightseers' balcony has been constructed along the entire length of the quayward side of the terminal, and further visitors' facilities are provided by a 100 ft tower at the south end.

CARGO AND PASSENGER TERMINAL, Berth 102

One of the eight mail boats of the Union Castle Mail Steamship Co. Ltd leaves Berth 102 at 4 p.m. every Thursday, and in order to provide essential facilities for this, together with other services to South Africa, the present building has been designed for the British Transport Commission and was officially opened in January 1956.

The foundations are supported on $17\frac{1}{2}''$ dia. and 20" dia. West's Shell Piles driven during 1952 to depths varying from 20 ft to 50 ft. Under the main supports, groups of 8 and 9 piles were installed to suit a maximum stanchion load of 800 tons and the total bearing capacity of the piles is 45,000 tons. Two 20" dia. piles 49 ft long were successfully test-loaded by the clients to 180 tons each.

The sub-strata in the area of Berth 102 consist of gravel fill overlying the natural ballast bed of the river and every endeavour was made to reach this ballast with the piles.

Our piles were driven amongst existing precast piles which had been installed about 1930 to support the original Shed 102, destroyed by enemy action in 1940, and the design of the foundations for the new building incorporates the use of the precast piles. Owing to consolidation of the gravel fill the driving was very difficult in certain places, particularly in the groups adjacent to the quay wall where penetration below its foundation was desirable but was not always possible.

The two-storey building is 932 ft long, 162 ft wide, and the height from the ground level to the highest part of the roof is 52 ft. The enclosed storage area for cargo on the upper floor extends the entire length of the building and has a width of 108 ft, while the adjoining crane bay and cargo landing platform measure 442 ft long by 20 ft wide, and 640 ft long by 34 ft wide respectively.

At the eastern end on the same level, passengers' friends are provided for by a balcony, access to which is by a stairway approached from the quayside.

On the ground floor at the eastern end a spacious waiting hall caters for the needs of passengers. The amenities in this hall include a buffet, bureaux de change, rail booking office, immigration room, telephone and writing rooms, a bookstall and other facilities. From the waiting hall passengers proceed into the Customs area and thence to the boat train or road departure platforms.

The building was designed and constructed under the supervision of the

Stewarts and Lloyds Ltd : Transit warehouse

Ocean Trading Co. Ltd : Warehouse

C. G. Hibbert & Co. Ltd : Warehouse extension

Below : Andrews (Southampton) Ltd : Garage

Docks Engineer, Mr. J. H. Jellett, O.B.E., M.I.C.E., with Messrs Scott & Wilson, Kirkpatrick & Partners acting as consultants for the structural steel framework and reinforced concrete floor.

TRANSIT WAREHOUSE, Stewarts and Lloyds Ltd

Stewarts and Lloyds is a well-known name in the British steel industry at home and overseas. The photograph shows their transit warehouse with tube storage pens, which has been erected since the war, at the New Docks. It stands on 92-$17\frac{1}{2}''$ dia. West's Shell Piles carrying some 50 tons each.

An extension to the first warehouse, which is nearly the same as the one shown, is supported by 69-$17\frac{1}{2}''$ dia. West's Shell Piles, average length 27 ft.

WAREHOUSE, The Ocean Trading Co. Ltd

The Ocean Trading Company's warehouse for which West's Piling designed and constructed the reinforced concrete floors and foundations is supported on 75-$17\frac{1}{2}''$ dia. West's Shell Piles. This Company runs a number of shops on board ship, where a variety of goods can be purchased, and these premises, situated outside the New Docks, contain a magnificent showroom.

The scheme was designed by Messrs W. H. Saunders & Son, the well-known architects of Southampton, Portsmouth and Coventry.

WAREHOUSE EXTENSION, C. G. Hibbert & Co. Ltd

Messrs C. G. Hibbert, a subsidiary of Simonds, the famous brewers of Reading, have a contract for the bottling of Simonds beer consumed on board ship, particularly on the *Queen Mary* and *Queen Elizabeth* trans-atlantic services.

Since the warehouse was built, before the war, West's Piling have carried out the reinforced concrete foundations for two substantial two-storey extensions, which embody 145-$17\frac{1}{2}''$ dia. West's Shell Piles. A further extension is contemplated when a new section for canning beer will be built.

The scheme was designed by Messrs W. H. Saunders & Son.

GARAGE, Andrews (Southampton) Ltd

Andrews have a garage inside Southampton Old Docks which is well known to those who store their cars when sailing from England via Southampton.

The photograph illustrates their branch within the boundary of the New Docks. Foundations in reinforced concrete comprising 47-$17\frac{1}{2}''$ dia. West's Shell Piles for the structure were designed and constructed by West's Piling.

Andrews' Garage has a monopoly inside the docks and is greatly concerned with the licensing and plating of cars belonging to foreign visitors. Furthermore, the garage offers a very efficient fuelling and repairing service.

Stafford : Access tunnel under construction

Below : Completed foundations

STAFFORD

FOUNDATIONS FOR FACTORY EXTENSION

This contract was carried out for the Universal Grinding Wheel Company Limited, who are one of the best known manufacturers of grinding wheels in this country. Their factory is the largest of its kind in Europe and one of the largest in the world. The new extension is part of an expansion and replacement scheme at the works, which occupies an area of 44 acres.

Although referred to generally as a " slab ", the foundation was considerably more complex. Substantial reinforcement was contained in the sections that were to sustain heavy machinery, and tunnels for both access and ventilation purposes were incorporated, all supported by a network of beams which were themselves founded on 364 West's Shell Piles, $17\frac{1}{2}''$ dia. The piles averaged 43 ft in length, the requisite set being obtained in red sandy marl after penetrating layers of peat, white marl, and white and red sand.

One of the noteworthy features of this contract was the size of the supporting beams, many being as much as 5 ft in depth. Their reinforcement was proportionately large, consisting of steel bars up to $1\frac{1}{2}$ in. dia. and requiring considerable handling care. The excavation that was necessary for all the beams and tunnels, when spread over the remainder of the site, raised the level of the entire area by 1 ft. The shuttering to the concrete was carried out in brickwork.

The upper photograph on the opposite page shows the 8 ft deep access tunnel under construction, and the lower view illustrates a portion of the completed slab where little can be seen of the complexities below except the row of rectangular holes which are the exhaust vents of the 6 ft deep ventilation tunnel beneath.

The Universal Grinding Wheel Company is a most progressive organization constantly seeking new ideas and methods, and great flexibility of operation was demanded from West's Piling, many design refinements and improvements being carried out during the progress of the contract.

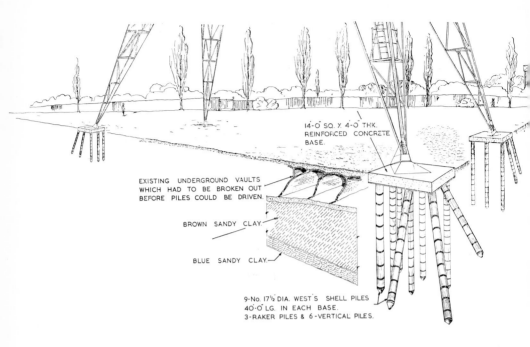

14-0" SQ. X 4-0" THK. REINFORCED CONCRETE BASE.

EXISTING UNDERGROUND VAULTS WHICH HAD TO BE BROKEN OUT BEFORE PILES COULD BE DRIVEN.

BROWN SANDY CLAY.

BLUE SANDY CLAY.

9-No. 17½ DIA. WEST'S SHELL PILES 40-0" LG. IN EACH BASE. 3-RAKER PILES & 6-VERTICAL PILES.

Crystal Palace : Diagrammatic view of piled foundations

Crystal Palace : Completed footing for tower leg

86

CRYSTAL PALACE

PILING AND FOUNDATIONS FOR
TELEVISION TOWER

This new 708-ft high tower is of the self-supporting type, standing on four legs similar to the Eiffel Tower. Each leg rests on a reinforced concrete footing and is held by an anchoring unit, incorporating the holding-down bolts cast in the concrete.

In view of the complexity of the stresses in a structure of this nature, which include uplift and horizontal thrust in addition to the normal vertical loading, each footing is supported by a combination of 6 vertical and 3 raker West's Shell Piles $17\frac{1}{2}''$ dia. The sub-strata and adjacent underground structures demanded piles of a length in the region of 40 ft. This entailed driving the piles a good depth into very firm clay and the resistance encountered in all piles was of a very high order.

The lower photograph (opposite) shows a completed footing. The holding-down bolts, with protective wrapping, can be seen protruding from the inclined pad.

This work was carried out in conjunction with British Insulated Callender's Construction Co. Ltd, for the British Broadcasting Corporation.

The completed tower
(Photo by courtesy of " The Times ")

87

Above : Pitsford—Chemical bunker foundation

Below: Close-up of bunker foundation showing Square Grip reinforcing steel

PITSFORD

PILING AND FOUNDATIONS FOR
WATER TREATMENT PLANT

Reproduced on the opposite page are two photographs of foundation work carried out by West's Piling, at Pitsford Reservoir, near Northampton.

In the foreground of the upper illustration is the chemical bunker foundation incorporating 25 West's Shell Piles, and beyond this, the levelled area containing 370 West's Shell Piles, ready for the water treatment plant foundation. All the piles driven were $17\frac{1}{2}''$ dia. and of 24 ft 6 in. average length.

The lower illustration is a close-up of the chemical bunker foundation and shows Square Grip reinforcing steel being fixed prior to concrete being placed. Accuracy to within $\frac{1}{8}$ in. both in level and in position was specified by the clients, the Mid-Northamptonshire Water Board.

All shuttering and formwork to the perimeter of the floor and pipe troughs was of wrought timber, but before this and the steel were fixed, 2 in. of concrete formed a covering to the site and exterior beam sides. The concrete could therefore be placed in one operation, avoiding construction joints and this method was greatly appreciated by our clients.

This reservoir and water treatment plant were opened by Her Majesty Queen Elizabeth, the Queen Mother, on 25th October, 1956.

Warrington : External view of new extrusion factory

Warrington : Piling in progress for extension

WARRINGTON

PILING FOR ALUMINIUM WORKS

The British Aluminium Company have been producing aluminium and aluminium alloy extrusions since 1911, and for many years this activity has been concentrated at their Warrington factory, which is also a sheet and strip rolling mill.

The Company's land at Latchford Locks totals 69·58 acres, of which the parent factory occupies some 4 acres. Adequate space existed, therefore, for the new extrusion factory which, with its subsidiary buildings, occupies 1·53 acres.

In view of the relatively heavy loading required in portions of this building, the foundations presented a special problem because of the poor bearing capacity of the ground. Test bore-holes showed that at least the top 20 ft of ground was composed of silt, peat and running sand and that the water table was only approximately 4 ft below ground level. It was, therefore, decided to disregard the top stratum for bearing purposes and to carry the loads on piles driven to an average depth of 40 ft into red marl, clay and sandstone.

The portion of the building in which the heavy plant was situated necessitated a loading of 15 cwt. per sq. ft for which $17\frac{1}{2}''$ dia. piles were driven on a grid of 6 ft 3 in. centres and the remainder on a grid of 8 ft 4 in. centres for a loading of $7\frac{1}{2}$ cwt. per sq. ft. Additional piles were inserted for the bases of the building stanchions. The $12\frac{1}{2}$ in. thick reinforced concrete floor throughout the building was designed as a beam spanning from the pile caps and attached to plant foundations where the thickness of these necessitated cutting off the piles at a lower level.

The main building, 550 ft long, is of steel construction designed to carry one 25-ton and two $7\frac{1}{2}$-ton cranes, the span between crane rails being 100 ft with a height to truss tie level of 30 ft.

Attached to the west side of the main building is a 40 ft wide toolroom, 100 ft long, which can be extended to 200 ft. Ancillary buildings comprise boiler-house, sub-station, office and lavatory accommodation.

Continuing the expansion of their extrusion capacity the British Aluminium Company Limited have also built a further extension to the west of the Latchford Locks Extrusion Works. The new building, 250 ft long by 106 ft span, is supported on $17\frac{1}{2}''$ dia. West's Shell Piles varying in length from 20 ft to 55 ft. The construction is similar to that of the parent factory—steel structure, with Freeman Morrison Dialindre aluminium wall cladding and Anderson E type aluminium roof decking.

Above : Denton—Producer foundations

Below : Denton—Coke hopper columns

DENTON

NEW GASWORKS SITE

Foundation work and reinforced concrete construction of considerable extent were undertaken on this site by West's Piling & Construction Company in connection with the new installation of 160 50-in. Glover-West retorts and associated plant at the Denton New Works of the North-Western Gas Board.

The earlier stages of the contract included the driving of 409 West's Shell Piles 17½″ dia. for the retort house and ancillary building foundations. The average length of the piles was nearly 24 ft.

In addition to the aforementioned, the contract also embraced reinforced concrete construction for the coke plant, bagging plant, ash skip hoist pit, associated buildings, etc., and tippler and breaker pits including their superstructure.

Below : Reinforced concrete work at Denton
(Coke grading plant in background)

BRISTOL

Above :

*Purification plant.
Some completed anti-vibration pump bases
for pump-house*

Below :

*Retort house. View
through ash conveyor
tunnel*

94

BRISTOL

GAS PLANT FOUNDATIONS

The extensive civil engineering construction programme, consisting of twelve separate contracts, carried out by West's Piling & Construction Company on the Stapleton Road Gasworks site, Bristol, was divided into three sections.

The first of these, for West's Gas Improvement Company, entailed the construction of a reinforced concrete foundation on marl for the new Glover-West plant of 128 50-in. retorts. These contracts included complicated tippler and ash pits, a series of ash conveyor tunnels and foundations for the retort house annexes. Large-scale site investigations were undertaken by the Company to prove the depth and bearing capacity of the hard marl strata. This information proved of great value in deciding upon the precautions necessary for dealing with the considerable water pressure when constructing deep pits.

The second section, for the South-Western Gas Board (Bristol Sub-Division), consisted of the construction of the foundations and superstructure for the liquid purification plant buildings together with the sludge treatment plant, pipe trestle and gantry foundations, the cooling tower pond and washing plant foundations. The liquid purification plant was partly founded on marl, but where the depth of this increased considerably, piling was necessary and 199-17$\frac{1}{2}$" dia. West's Shell Piles were driven through fill of varying thickness. The average length of piles was a little over 20 ft.

The third and most recent contract provided a piled foundation for the Gastechnik Plant—this was also carried out for the Bristol Sub-Division of the South-Western Gas Board.

Bournville : Piling in progress

Bournville : Completed building

BOURNVILLE

WATERSIDE STORES

The foundations for a new " crumb " and paper stores, 38,000 sq. ft in area, were constructed under extremely severe weather conditions in eight months for Messrs Cadbury Bros. A total of 501-20″ dia. West's Shell Piles were driven through made-up ground, consolidated over a period of 35 years, to boulder clay to depths ranging from 30 ft to 70 ft. Full advantage was taken of the adaptability of the West's pile by designing the slab so that maximum load, with regard to length, was transferred to every pile. This was done by varying the spacing of piles supporting the floor, of flat slab construction and designed for a loading of 10 cwt. per sq. ft. The portal frames and brick walls were carried on independent reinforced concrete beams—a special fixing being designed in these beams to take the heavy horizontal reactions and moments at the feet of the frames.

Much ingenuity was required to get the 43RB base machine on to the site due to very narrow access facilities and the poor condition of the ground. The 43RB was off-loaded on the road from a road-borne low-loading trailer and " squeezed " through the main entrance gates, thence travelling under its own power on to a rail-borne low-loading wagon. The client's own locomotives moved this 87-ton load to their Waterside Factory from whence it travelled on sleepers to the site.

Many foundation problems arose on the site, including hard driving and the presence of massive obstructions in the filled material. Co-operation and sympathetic assistance from Messrs Cadbury Bros.' Engineers Department did undoubtedly help progress, and was much appreciated.

NORTHOLT

OFFICE BLOCK, PLANT SHOP, ENGINE TEST HOUSE

Piling for an office block and plant shop for Messrs Taylor Woodrow Construction Ltd was completed in August 1949, and a total of 174 West's Shell Piles $17\frac{1}{2}''$ dia. were driven. Pile lengths varied from 20 ft to 49 ft 6 in. a feature presenting no difficulty to West's Shell Piling System. Reference to the plan reveals the reason for this wide variation in length.

The site, although levelled with cinders and brick rubble fill, was formerly that of an old brickworks and the Plant Shop was actually sited halfway over the edge of a claypit, where the longest piles occurred.

An additional 18 piles were driven over the claypit area to an average depth of 37 ft for the foundations to the Engine Test House.

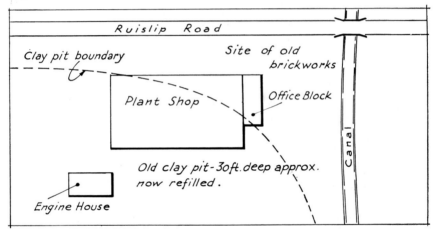

Above : Plan of site   *Below : Completed offices and plant shop*

POPLAR

CHURCH OF ST. MARY AND ST. JOSEPH

The reinforced concrete piled foundation for this church, one of the largest and most important to be built in this country since the war, was constructed by West's Piling. The foundation incorporates 126 West's Shell Piles $17\frac{1}{2}''$ dia., the average depth of penetration being 30 ft. Eight bored piles were also included.

The Architect was Mr Adrian Gilbert Scott, C.B.E., M.C., F.R.I.B.A., the Consulting Engineer was Mr Burnard Geen, M.Inst.C.E., and the Main Contractors were John Mowlem & Co. Ltd.

READING

REINFORCED CONCRETE WATER TOWER

In the Autumn of 1952 the reinforced concrete water tower illustrated on this page was constructed by West's Piling at Reading Gasworks on a foundation incorporating 8-17$\frac{1}{2}$" dia. piles suitable for a loading of 56 tons per pile.

Plywood shuttering specially designed by West's Piling was employed on the tower and the resulting finish on the concrete was notably smooth and even.

The tank, capacity 56,000 gals., was subjected to a 21-day water test, with completely satisfactory results.

READING

*Completed
water tower*

BILLINGHAM. SULPHURIC ACID PLANT

Built on a piled foundation incorporating $17\frac{1}{2}''$ dia. West's Shell Piles
(*Photograph by courtesy of I.C.I. Ltd*)

**SILVERTOWN,
PLAISTOW
WHARF**

SUGAR SILO

*This 40,000-ton
capacity Weibull
sugar storage
silo is built on
20'' dia. West's
Shell Piles.*

(*Photograph by
courtesy of
Tate & Lyle Ltd*)

Palais du Centenaire. Above : Steel reinforcement and shuttering being assembled on steel arch centering, prior to casting front pair of concrete arches. Below : Completed building

BRUSSELS

PALAIS DU CENTENAIRE

Belgium assumed its independence in 1835 and has since made a tradition of celebrating this occasion every 50 years by holding an International Trade Exhibition in Brussels.

For this, every half century, a permanent Exhibition Hall, called a Palace, is built. The Century Palace, built in 1933/35 and located in north-west Brussels, stands on West's Shell Piles, of which 50 per cent. were rakers.

The pile lengths were of the order of 45 ft with the toes bedded in stiff clay. The raker piles were driven at a rake of 1 in 2 and, together with the heavy capping, acted as abutments for the arches. The building is 280 ft wide, 700 ft long and 145 ft high, made up structurally of twelve reinforced concrete three-hinged arches, spanning the full width and constructed in pairs with an expansion joint every 70 ft.

It is interesting to note that the working loads on the piles were at their greatest during the construction of the building, i.e. when the concrete arches were cast and during the maturing period of the concrete, while the steel centering used for their construction weighing some 600 tons was still in position. To release and move the steel centering bodily, the concrete arches, once matured, were freed from their supports by opening them at their top hinges, by means of horizontal jacks. This allowed the arches to be raised by pivoting on their spherical bottom hinges and thus freed them from the centering which slid out bodily on rollers.

The construction, which started in the summer of 1933, was completed in 1935, and included two other smaller permanent structures on either side of the main hall, one of which stands on West's Shell Piles.

This hall is continuously used for exhibitions and is a familiar sight to visitors. It is a precious landmark in this ancient city, of which Belgians are very proud, being a very imposing and spacious structure of great beauty.

CHAPTER FIVE

FROM OTHER SOURCES

WE are grateful to the Editors concerned for their permission to reproduce the following extracts from publications and technical articles dealing with West's Shell Piling System.

From " The Steel Company of Wales Limited—A Technical Survey "— Trostre Works Section—a special issue of " The Iron and Coal Trades Review."

Messrs Robert M. Douglas (Contractors) Ltd, on " Civil Engineering for Trostre Works " :

PILING

With the exception of the 5-stand tandem mill, the temper mills and palm oil recovery building, the whole plant, with minor exceptions, is supported on piles. About 25,000 piles, averaging 25 ft long, were driven, i.e. about 120 miles of piling.

West's pile system was adopted for all piles and in this Company's experience has proved speedy, effective, and adaptable. As many as 15 pile frames were working on a fairly limited area, and it was necessary to have much more manœuvrability than would have been provided by the standard type of pile frame on rollers or castors ; therefore only two of this latter type were used, the remaining machines being either crawler cranes with hanging leaders or lorry mounted frames. Pile shells were cast on the site under cover of temporary corrugated sheet structures. This avoided interruptions by inclement weather. In all, at the peak about 500 shell moulds were used continuously.

Due to the presence of acidity and aggressive waters in the sub-strata, particularly where peat was present, all pile shells and pile shoes up to + 6·00 o.d. were cast in aluminous cement using pennant stone. All other shells were cast using rapidly hardening cement and mountain limestone. A very severe set was specified. Tests showed that precast piles and the West pile gave the same results in penetration and bearing capacity.

Messrs L. G. Mouchel & Partners on "Civil Engineering Design for Construction of Main Foundations":

PILING

The extraordinary number of piles involved clearly indicates some form of pattern piling, though the extent of this can easily be misjudged. General floors and basements subject to uniform loadings were naturally treated in this manner, the heavy floor loadings often requiring the piles to be driven at close centres. For instance, those under the roll shop were at 4-ft 5-in. centres, and in the groups under the Personnel Tunnel at 3-ft centres. Elsewhere, however, it was often necessary to design each pile separately over a large area to allow for machine loadings. It will also be seen that the method of incorporating the pile in the ferro-concrete structure which it supports varied widely, pile caps being in some instances dispensed with altogether.

In addition, some of the difficulties encountered in the actual driving had a marked effect not only on subsequent designs but also frequently necessitated a new approach to those already under construction. Early test loadings, for instance, established that ground conditions would not permit the estimated working load of 60 tons per pile which had then to be reduced to 50 tons.

Over a certain area of the site it was necessary to take special precautions as it was found that piles could be driven to a set, but that with additional driving they often penetrated several feet further. In order to define this area, a series of exploratory probings was carried out by driving down the steel mandrel fitted with a steel shoe.

It is interesting to note that a 14-in. $\times$ 14-in. precast pile was driven in this area and its behaviour during driving and the penetration and set obtained were not markedly different from those for the West's piles.

As a result of this experience it was agreed to drive the piles to a much more severe set than had originally been determined by using the Hiley Formula. For instance, according to this formula, a 30-ft pile should have a set of six blows to the last inch, using a 3-ton hammer with a 33-in. drop, whereas the sets used were of the order of 25 blows to the last inch. This is not to be taken as implying that the Hiley Formula was misleading, but rather as an indication of how the very special conditions which were encountered at Trostre led to modifications. Individual piles driven to the formula gave extremely good test-load results.

It is probable that the close centres at which the piles had to be driven led to a considerable modification in the ground texture and also to some disturbance of piles previously driven. Provision for these factors was not made in the formula.

When pile driving first started the only information available was for the groups of piles under the main piers. These piles were all in the first class above. Those in the second class generally behaved in a normal manner except that, owing to their concentrated spacing, the fill became extremely compacted and the driving in consequence harder. However, the piles stood up to heavy driving with only the normal shell breakages.

TEST LOADS

Throughout the period of driving, test loadings were made, the piles being capped in Ciment Fondu and the test loads of steel ingots applied on a steel grillage. The following is a typical result : Length of pile 34 ft, settlement under 50 tons, 0·16 in., and settlement under 75 tons, 0·26 in.

It was eventually found that there existed a definite relationship between the date of driving, the date of testing, and the result. The greater the gap between the two dates, the more satisfactory the result.

Any pile which drifted over 8 in. out of position required special treatment in the pile caps, unless it was at the centre of a group. Those which drifted more than 1 in 10 out of the vertical were generally replaced, unless some other factors enabled them to be accepted.

Table I gives an indication of the quantities involved :

TABLE I. *Data on Piling Quantities*

	Number of Piles Driven	Total Length
Main buildings	24,653	534,072 ft
Other buildings and drainage work	1,072	27,765 ft
Total	25,725	561,837 ft

During the main part of the work 13 frames drove an average of 75 piles per day.

The piles themselves are further described in editorial matter under the heading : " How the plant was built and equipped ".

In May 1947 piling operations were commenced, and in a period of less than three years this Company drove approximately 32,000 piles on the sites of the 80-in. hot-strip mill at Abbey Works, Margam, and for the new cold reduction mill at Trostre. At Abbey Works, activities were located in the mill area, the mould preparation shop and the ingot stripping and stocking department, as well as on drainage piling. In the former cases steam frames were principally used, as the piles were all located in a reasonably small area, and not a great deal of moving was involved. For the drainage piling, however, where the work was spread over a large area, excavator type mobile rigs were used, and these were ideal for the purpose as they could travel from site to site in the shortest possible time. At Margam Works the piling was carried out with mobile rigs and consisted of piling amongst existing buildings where headroom was often limited. For this work the smaller mobile machines were very suitable. The work carried out in this part of the works was for new tipplers, boiler-house and pump-house, intake flume and water mains as well as an extension to the existing ore bunkers.

Complementary to the foregoing, a further contract of piling was completed for the then Great Western Railway at Margam. This work comprised piling to the north abutment and retaining walls of a flyover crossing over the main London–South Wales line. The site was of a very restricted nature and mobile rigs were used.

TROSTRE WORKS

The contract at Trostre Works was opened in September 1947, but it was not until February 1948 that full-scale piling operations commenced. In its first phase, 25,500 piles were driven and these were completed by March 1950. At the peak, twelve machines were in operation, ten of which were of the mobile type. This high percentage of mobile outfits permitted extreme latitude in planning and releasing information, in that at short notice activities could be diverted to new sites. The very high programme figure of 1,500 piles per month was easily maintained during the peak period and the piling was completed to schedule.

In the second phase of the Trostre piling, preparation for the remaining ancillary buildings was completed.

Throughout these contracts the piles were driven to exceedingly good sets. At Margam an average depth of 30 ft was obtained, while at Trostre the pile shoes were driven into shaly rock over all parts of the site where the depth varied from 7 ft 6 in. to 80 ft.

Ciment Fondu was used extensively in making the increment pile shells on both sites. At Margam the object of its use was to obtain large stocks of matured shells in the least possible time, while at Trostre the consulting engineer specified composite Fondu-Portland piles. The object of this was to provide the lower part of the pile in Ciment Fondu as a protection against deleterious organic acids, and the upper part in Portland cement where the danger was not present.

Extract from " Civil Engineering at Trostre Works " by A. J. Williams, A.M.I.Mech.E., published in " The Iron and Coal Trades Review," October 1st, 1952.

PILING

The pile selected having regard to the number and rate of progress required, was of the shell type. This pile consists of precast reinforced concrete shells $17\frac{1}{2}$ in. o.d., 12 in. i.d. and 3 ft long. The shells are threaded on a vertical steel mandrel with a reinforced concrete shoe at the bottom, and driven into the ground to a predetermined set ; the bottom of the mandrel bears on the top of the shoe so that the force of the drive is transmitted direct to the shoe, while the shells are driven by means of a special driving head placed at the top of the mandrel in such a way as to exert pressure on the top of the shells in order that they fall at the same rate as the shoe.

The heavy floor loadings often required the piles to be driven at close centres ; those under the roll shop were at 4-ft 5-in. centres and in the groups (under the personnel tunnel) at 3-ft centres, while it was often necessary to design each pile separately over a large area to allow for machine loadings.

The piles driven may be roughly divided into three classes : First, those driven through a 3-ft thick ash carpet laid on the original ground, to accommodate basements of average depth ; the second comprises piles driven through a 13-ft thick ash filling laid on the original ground under areas without basements and, finally, those driven through a 3-ft thick ash carpet laid at the bottom of excavations taken down below the original ground level to accommodate deep basements.

Altogether, nearly 26,000 piles were driven and at the peak of this operation as many as 13 pile frames were in use at one time. The average length of piles is about 24 ft, giving a total of about 120 miles of piling, and a detailed record has been kept of every pile driven.

Extracts from "Contractors' Record and Municipal Engineering," *January 28th, 1953.*

Mr. Rolt Hammond, A.C.G.I., A.M.I.C.E., in " Some Notes on Piling ", says :

The author has had experience on large construction works of both the West's Shell Pile and the Franki Pile. In the shell-piling system tubular shells of reinforced concrete are threaded on a tubular steel mandrel, which drives a concrete shoe into the ground. A cushioned spring collar around the top of the mandrel bears on the uppermost shell to ensure that the whole shell column will follow the shoe into the ground. Joints between shells are sealed with bitumen, and when driving has been completed the whole inside of the pile can be inspected before concrete and reinforcement are introduced.

A very interesting modification of the West's shell-piling system was employed in 1938, under the direction of Mr. J. W. Curtis, M.B.E., A.M.I.Mech.E., for driving piles forming the foundation for a new extension to a college at Oxford. The rig employed consisted of a movable under-carriage, on which was mounted kentledge weighing about 120 tons and against which a hydraulically operated jack with a stroke of 12 in. was used to force a shoe and standard shell units into the ground, some 66 piles being driven in this manner to an average depth of 27 ft.

This jacking method was employed in order to avoid any vibration being transmitted through the ground to adjacent college structures of historic value, the site being within the grounds of New College, close to the Bell Tower, the latter built in sand and mortar on a foundation of brushwood ; the strata were heavily waterlogged and there was a maximum depth of 25 ft of running sand. Bored piles, although they would have been free from vibration during construction, were not considered to be suitable because of the fluid nature of the underlying sand stratum which might have been removed during the process of boring, design of the pile having to be of a type which would provide adequate lateral strength.

The maximum resistance of 120 tons was reached at depths ranging from 26 ft to 28 ft, the hydraulic jack being operated by a small petrol pump, a pressure gauge indicating the load applied to the pile. During pushing down of the first 10 ft or 12 ft a resistance of between 30 and 40 tons was experienced, and only during the last foot or so was anything approaching the full weight of the kentledge approached. Each pile was a tested pile so far as bearing capacity was concerned, and on one or two occasions two piles a day were jacked down. The reinforced concrete shaft of each pile ensured that there was adequate lateral strength in this fluid sub-soil.

" Building Strong Foundations," extracted from " Motor Transport ",
October 25th, 1952.

The new oil refinery at Fawley, the recently completed steelworks at Llanelly, South Wales, gasworks, blocks of flats, and ordinary houses are among the buildings which rest on foundations laid by West's Piling & Construction Co. Ltd, of Harmondsworth, Middlesex.

The foundations consist of precast concrete pile units which are driven into soft ground to the required depth. This required depth obviously varies from site to site in different parts of the country, depending on the geological nature of the ground. In order to allow for this factor and at the same time facilitate handling and transport, the piles consist of individual shells all weighing over 3 cwt. each but slightly varying as to size and diameter. They have all been precast in three standard sizes : 3 ft long by $17\frac{1}{2}$ in. diameter, 3 ft long by 20 in. diameter and 4 ft long by $14\frac{1}{2}$ in. diameter. These piles are knocked into the ground by a 3-ton hammer which, with its mandrels, is held aloft by the swan neck jib and tubular leaders of the tracked mobile base machine—the whole outfit being known as a piling frame. Many of these machines of Ruston Bucyrus manufacture, are in service with the Company. Ancillary loose plant required on the site of operations includes cement mixers, pumps and wheelbarrows.

All this equipment—hammers, tubular leaders, base machines, and loose plant—is based at the Harmondsworth depot on the London–Bath road facing the western end of London Airport.

To move it from the plant depot to the place of work, which may be anywhere in England, Scotland or Wales, the Company uses heavy haulage contractors for the base machines and its own fleet of " C " licensed vehicles for the remainder.

Three main factors dictate the manner in which any task undertaken by the firm is tackled. First, that of distance. If the site of the projected construction work is more than 100 miles from Harmondsworth then the shells will be made on the spot and not conveyed by means of a shuttle service from the plant depot. Secondly, before any work can start at a site it is essential for a base machine to be present, as only by the use of one of these can the hammers and mandrels be lifted off the vehicle on which they arrive. As the base machines are transported to and from the sites by outside haulage contractors, a high degree of co-ordination is called for to ensure that all the equipment arrives in the correct order at the scheduled time.

However, perfect co-ordination, no matter how earnestly sought after by all concerned, cannot always be achieved and therefore it needs to be supplemented by a third factor—flexibility. Thus, if no alternative arrangements

A Bedford tractor with the low-loading semi-trailer manœuvres into position prior to loading at the Harmondsworth depot. Shells can be seen stacked in the background

The swan-neck jib of a piling frame is loaded on to a 5-ton Bedford truck

can be made, as may often be the case, to prevent the hammer and mandrels, the swan-neck jib and the tubular leaders of the base machine arriving at a site before the machine itself, then an articulated vehicle will be used. This will unhitch its semi-trailer at the site and return to base where, no doubt, it can be usefully employed in conjunction with the spare semi-trailer. This spare low-loading semi-trailer is a new outfit acquired by the Company as an experiment with the object of testing the merits of independent tractive units.

The need for flexibilty is also the reason which has justified the Company operating its own fleet of vehicles on all except the heaviest work. In particular this applies to the supply of shells to points within the 100 miles radius, as in the case of these shorter distances the shells are delivered by a shuttle service from Harmondsworth and on arrival are stacked in heaps at points very near to the actual ground where the foreman concerned anticipates he will need them. It is, therefore, easy to imagine the disorganization and resultant waste of mileage, time and materials which might be involved were work to be delayed for several hours, or indeed a day or two, as it often is after heavy rain.

When such a situation arises the foreman immediately reports by telephone to the plant depot and stops the flow of materials. Vehicles that are already well on the way are met on their arrival and, provided that their loads are not required, are diverted elsewhere according to instructions from the base. The supply of shells thus continues to flow to places where they are needed without the danger of a large stock being dumped at a site where work has temporarily ceased and where the total number of shells required for the completion of the job may fall well short of the number provided.

The service vans are manned by skilled fitters who constantly circulate between the sites all over the country on which the firm's vehicles, machinery and loose plant are employed. Each man is fully equipped with all the hand tools necessary for undertaking emergency repairs, plus essential spares such as batteries and sparking plugs. These fitters are often away from their Harmondsworth base for weeks at a time.

General maintenance of the vehicles, and major repairs, are carried out at Harmondsworth by a Motor Transport Department.

A large, modern, mobile piling outfit, developed by West's Piling and based on a diesel-powered excavator

Left :

*The West's Piling
display at the
National Fuel
Efficiency Exhibition,
Manchester, 1953*

Right :

*Building and
Public Works
Exhibition, Paris,
1956. Display
by Compagnie
Générale de
Construction de
Fours for
West's Shell
Piles*

The following extract is taken from a leaflet on West's Shell Piling System published by our Continental Licensee, Compagnie Générale de Construction de Fours, 8 place des États Unis, Montrouge (Seine), France.

LE PIEU WEST

DESCRIPTION DU PROCÉDÉ

Le pieu West est un pieu coulé dans le sol dont le fourreau est constitué par des éléments tubulaires préfabriqués en béton armé (gaines).

Les opérations successives pour l'exécution d'un pieu sont les suivantes :

1. Les gaines sont enfilées sur un mandrin en acier reposant lui-même sur un sabot en béton ; des colliers en tôle assurent la jonction entre les différents éléments, l'étanchéité des joints étant obtenue par interposition de mastic.

2. L'enfoncement du pieu est obtenu par la chute d'un mouton de 3 à 5 tonnes sur une tête de battage spéciale. Celle-ci transmet directement au mandrin, donc à la pointe, l'énergie produite par le choc du mouton, alors qu'une partie seulement de l'effort est transmise aux gaines et assure leur enfoncement à la suite du sabot. Un réglage prévu sur la tête de battage permet d'adapter la valeur de cet effort à la résistance par frottement opposée par le sol à l'enfoncement des gaines.

3. Au cours du battage, de nouvelles gaines sont mises en place, après allongement du mandrin, et le battage est poursuivi jusqu'à la profondeur nécessaire.

4. Le mandrin étant retiré, l'intérieur des gaines est contrôlé, des armatures métalliques sont mises en place, et l'on procède au bétonnage du pieu

Trois types de pieux sont couramment employés :

Charge	Diamètre extérieur	Diamètre intérieur des gaines
Pieu de 30 à 40 T . . .	380 mm	280 mm
Pieu de 50 à 60 T . . .	450 mm	312 mm
Pieu de 80 à 100 T . . .	525 mm	380 mm

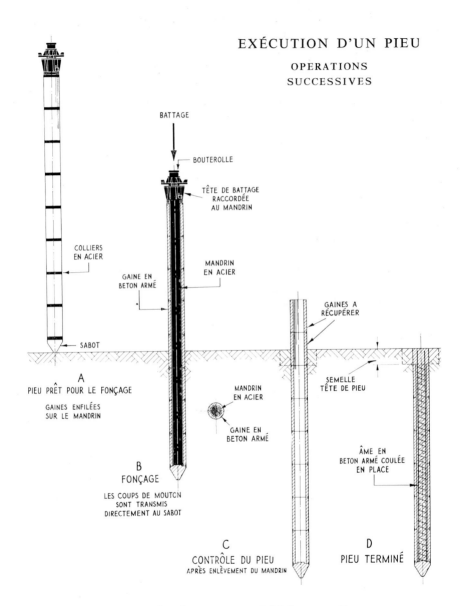

EXÉCUTION D'UN PIEU

OPERATIONS
SUCCESSIVES

BATTAGE

BOUTEROLLE

TÊTE DE BATTAGE
RACCORDÉE
AU MANDRIN

COLLIERS
EN ACIER

MANDRIN
EN ACIER

GAINE EN
BETON ARMÉ

GAINES A
RÉCUPÉRER

SABOT

A
PIEU PRÊT POUR LE FONÇAGE

GAINES ENFILÉES
SUR LE MANDRIN

MANDRIN
EN ACIER

SEMELLE
TÊTE DE PIEU

GAINE EN
BETON ARMÉ

ÂME EN
BETON ARMÉ COULÉE
EN PLACE

B
FONÇAGE

LES COUPS DE MOUTON
SONT TRANSMIS
DIRECTEMENT AU SABOT

C
CONTRÔLE DU PIEU
APRÈS ENLÈVEMENT DU MANDRIN

D
PIEU TERMINÉ

Diagram showing sequence of driving operations

116

Le pieu West est un pieu mixte, puisqu'il est à la fois " préfabriqué " et coulé en place. Il présente simultanément les principaux avantages des pieux préfabriqués et des pieux coulés en place sans en avoir les inconvénients :

1. La force portante du pieu peut être déterminée de façon précise par la mesure du refus en fin de battage ; il est possible de déterminer séparément les valeurs de la résistance de pointe et du frottement latéral.

2. Il est inutile de prévoir à l'avance jusqu'à quelle profondeur sera poursuivi le battage, puisque l'allongement progressif du pieu en cours d'exécution permet d'atteindre la couche de terrain résistant, quelque soit son niveau.

3. On peut contrôler avant le bétonnage l'intérieur du fourreau ; on a ainsi la certitude d'obtenir *un pieu sain, droit, de composition homogène* et de *section constante* en tous points. C'est la raison pour laquelle le pieu West est parmi les pieux couramment utilisés, celui qui offre la plus grande sécurité.

4. Le bétonnage du pieu peut être arrêté à un niveau quelconque et les gaines situées au-dessus de ce niveau peuvent être récupérées lors de l'exécution des terrassements.

5. Tous les pieux, quelles que soient leur longuer et leur section, peuvent être exécutés avec la même machine, ce qui permet de conduire rapidement et rationnellement les travaux.

Un stock important de gaines permet de commencer les travaux dans les plus brefs délais.

MADE AND PRINTED IN GREAT BRITAIN BY
HAMMOND & GRIFFITHS LTD